This edition published by Parragon Books Ltd in 2015

Parragon Books Ltd
Chartist House
15–17 Trim Street
Bath BA1 1HA, UK
www.parragon.com

ISBN 978-1-4723-9685-3

Printed in China

MONSTER HIGH

MONSTER HIGH

COLLECTION

PaRragon

Bath • New York • Cologne • Melbourne • Delhi
Hong Kong • Shenzhen • Singapore • Amsterdam

Frankie Stein™

Draculaura™

Age:
How many days has it been now?

Fave subject:
Hiss-tory

Worst subject:
Swimming – electricity
and water don't mix.

GFFs:
Draculaura and Clawdeen Wolf

Extra-scare-icular activities:
Fearleading squad.

I'm never without ...
high-voltage hair! My black and
white streaks are hard to miss.

I'm always saying ...
"bolts!"

My ghoulfriends say I'm ...
electrifyingly enthusiastic
and scarily stylish.

Age:
1,600

Fave subject:
Creative writing

Worst subject:
Ge-ogre-phy

GFFs:
Frankie Stein and Clawdeen Wolf

Extra-scare-icular activities:
Fearleading squad;
Newspaper Club president.

I'm never without ...
Count Fabulous™, my BFF – that's Bat
Friend Forever. Oh, and a make-up bag
full of 'Fierce & Flawless' products.

I'm always saying ...
"fangtastic!"

My ghoulfriends say I'm ...
the most fiendishly friendly
vampire around.

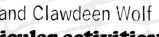

Clawdeen Wolf™

Age:
15

Fave subject:
Economics – I'm going to set up my own fashion empire.

Worst subject:
Physical dead-ucation (they won't let me wear my heels).

GFFs:
Draculaura and Frankie Stein

Extra-scare-icular activities:
Fearleading squad; football team; track team; Fashion Entrepreneur Club.

I'm never without ...
the latest hot bag or shoes – a ghoul can never have too many ughsome accessories.

I'm always saying ...
"clawsome!"

My ghoulfriends say I'm ...
a fierce fashionista who's loyal to the claw.

Cleo de Nile™

Age:
5,843 (give or take a few years)

Fave subject:
Geometry (it involves pyramid shapes).

Worst subject:
Hiss-tory – been there, seen that!

GFFs:
Ghoulia Yelps, and Deuce Gorgon is my boyfriend.

Extra-scare-icular activities:
Captain of the fearleading squad.

I'm never without ...
my bag of cursed icons – I never know when I might need them.

I'm always saying ...
"oh my Ra!"

My ghoulfriends say I'm ...
the most golden and talented head fearleader ... ever!

Lagoona Blue™

Fave subject:
Oceanography of course!
Worst subject:
Geology
GFFs:
Frankie, Clawdeen, Draculaura, Cleo, Abbey ... I'm a friendly kind of ghoul.
Extra-scare-icular activities:
Swim team captain.
I'm never without ...
a tube of monsturizer – I don't want my skin to dry up when I'm out of the water.
I'm always saying ...
"something's fishy!"
My ghoulfriends say I'm ...
a creepy-calm and caring crusader.

Ghoulia Yelps™

Age:
16 (monster years)
Fave subject:
This is like asking me to choose which one of my zombie relatives I prefer! I love them all equally.
Worst subject:
There is something to be learned from every class. Even dodgeball teaches one to duck.
GFFs:
Cleo de Nile and Spectra Vondergeist
Extra-scare-icular activities:
Comic Book Club president.
I'm never without ...
my schedule – it's even synced to my iCoffin!
I'm always saying ...
"uggh ruuur!"
My ghoulfriends say I'm ...
frighteningly clever.

Abbey Bominable™

Age:
16

Fave subject:
Maths

Worst subject:
Drama – only kind of scene I like is view of mountains.

GFFs:
Lagoona Blue and Frankie Stein

Extra-scare-icular activities:
Snowboarding team captain.

I'm never without ...
my ice-crystal necklace – it cools air around me so I am not getting too hot.

I'm always saying ...
"cool it!"

My ghoulfriends say I'm ...
strong and very long – I mean to say tall. And have warm heart under icy touch.

Spectra Vondergeist™

Age:
16

Fave subject:
Journalism – it runs through the places where my veins used to be.

Worst subject:
Maths – it's never open to interpretation.

GFFs:
Ghoulia Yelps

Extra-scare-icular activities:
Newspaper Club (weekly column 'Oh My Oracle' and online blog 'The Ghost Post').

I'm never without ...
my camera and iCoffin – I don't want to miss a monster scoop!

I'm always saying ...
"I've been waiting my entire death to cover a story like this!"

My ghoulfriends say I'm ...
a ghostly gossip guru.

9

Student Bodies

Robecca Steam™

Age:
116
Fave subject:
Metalwork
Worst subject:
Home ick – although I'm fangtastic at boiling water!
GFFs:
Rochelle Goyle and Frankie Stein
Extra-scare-icular activities:
Skultimate Roller Maze.
I'm never without ...
a set of spanners and my rocket boots, which are great for pulling scary-cool stunts.
I'm always saying ...
"full scream ahead!"
My ghoulfriends say I'm ...
the school scare-devil.

Rochelle Goyle™

Age:
415
Fave subject:
Architecture
Worst subject:
Swimming – I sink like stone.
GFFs:
Ghoulia Yelps, Robecca Steam and Venus McFlytrap
Extra-scare-icular activities:
Skultimate Roller Maze.
I'm never without ...
a book – I've loved reading ever since my family chose to protect the Monster High library.
I'm always saying ...
"travel beyond the stone you sit on."
My ghoulfriends say I'm ...
horribly hard-headed and dead-fully protective.

Venus McFlytrap™

Age:
15
Fave subject:
Biteology
Worst subject:
Woodwork – I can hear the screams when the saw goes in.
GFFs:
Lagoona, Robecca, Rochelle, Frankie and Ghoulia
Extra-scare-icular activities:
Chairmonster of the Monster High Green Party.
I'm never without ...
my pollens of persuasion – they have a funny effect on those around me.
I'm always saying ...
"don't be a loser, be a reuser!"
My ghoulfriends say I'm ...
a loveable tree-hugger who leads by example.

Deuce Gorgon™

Age:
16
Fave subject:
Home ick – it's the best class at Monster High.
Worst subject:
Home ick – I pretend to hate it!
BFFs:
Jackson Jekyll is my beast bud and Cleo de Nile is my ughsome ghoulfriend.
Extra-scare-icular activities:
Casketball team (guard).
I'm never without ...
my shades – otherwise it's a rockin' day at Monster High, you get me?
I'm always saying ...
"hey monster, what's up?"
My friends say I'm ...
a scary-cool skater dude with attitude.

Skelita Calaveras™

Age:
15

Fave subject:
Home ick. It's almost like
not being in class at all!

Worst subject:
Music. I couldn't carry a tune in a casket.

GFFs:
Jinafire Long and Clawdeen Wolf

Extra-scare-icular activities:
Anything associated with
Día de los Muertos.

I'm never without ...
sugar skulls! My favourite treat.

I'm always saying ...
"kindness to the bone!"

My ghoulfriends say I'm ...
always looking for
an excuse to skelebrate!

Jinafire Long™

Age:
15 hundred scales

Fave subject:
Metal shop. I love creating
steel sculptures.

Worst subject:
Physical dead-ucation.
Sweat makes my scales itch.

GFFs:
Skelita Calaveras and Clawdeen Wolf

Extra-scare-icular activities:
Calligraphy – it helps me to relax.

I'm never without ...
my sketchbook, for new ideas.

I'm always saying ...
"the spicier the better!"

My ghoulfriends say I'm ...
strong-willed, hot-tempered,
but always willing to lend a hand.

Howleen Wolf™

Age:
14

Fave subject:
I kind of like maths and sometimes hiss-tory … or biteology.

Worst subject:
It changes every day. Weird, huh?

GFFs:
Abbey Bominable and Clawdeen Wolf

Extra-scare-icular activities:
I love playing football.
It's so much fun!

I'm never without …
Cushion™, my pet hedgehog.

I'm always saying …
"I want to howl at my own moon."

My ghoulfriends say I'm …
not just Clawdeen's little sister!

Gigi Grant™

Age:
Dad says I'm 15, but he lost my birth certificate somewhere between Darius the Great and Julius Caesar, so I'm not sure.

Fave subject:
Astronomy – I love space!

Worst subject:
Driver's ed. The car is too small!

GFFs:
I wish I could name just a few!

Extra-scare-icular activities:
Sightseeing.

I'm never without …
some of my father's secret-recipe hummus. Yum!

I'm always saying …
"this is a wish come true!"

My ghoulfriends say I'm …
the kind of ghoul who detests being bottled up!

Twyla ™

Age:
15
Fave subject:
Psychology – it helps me
to make it through the night.
Worst subject:
Anything that involves
public speaking.
GFFs:
Spectra Vondergeist and Howleen Wolf
Extra-scare-icular activities:
Capturing normie nightmares.
I'm never without ...
a 'blurple' accessory.
I'm always saying ...
"be a boo-tiful dreamer!"
My ghoulfriends say I'm ...
a shadowy figure.

Honey Swamp ™

Age:
115 (in swamp monster years)
Fave subject:
Cinemat-ogre-phy.
I love learning new tricks.
Worst subject:
Home ick. Darlin' I already
know how to cook.
GFFs:
Viperine Gorgon and Clawdia Wolf
Extra-scare-icular activities:
I am a photographer. I do not *want* to
be one, you understand, I *am* one.
I'm never without ...
my camera.
I'm always saying ...
"there's always time to do it right."
My ghoulfriends say I'm ...
a perfectionist.

Age: 19

Fave subject: Philosophy of Screamplay Structure – it sounds boring but it's really creepy cool!

Worst subject: Art. I can write my ideas, but I certainly can't draw them!

GFFs: My brothers and sisters.

Extra-scare-icular activities: Writing! I write every day 'cause if you don't write, you can't call yourself a writer.

My ghoulfriends say I'm ... the one with the 'clumsy gene' in our family.

Clawdia Wolf ™

Age: 17

Fave subject: Art. Painting, sculpting and colour theory skills all come in handy when doing make-up.

Worst subject: Maths. Oh, I'm good at it, it's just not my favourite.

GFFs: Elissabat and Honey Swamp.

Extra-scare-icular activities: I love doing, shopping for and experimenting with make-up.

My ghoulfriends say I'm ... a boho-chic hippie ghoul.

Viperine Gorgon ™

Age: 1,601 years old

Fave subject: Drama. I have trained with the finest acting coaches in the world.

Worst subject: Physical dead-ucation. I suppose it would be okay if I could use a stunt monster to take my place....

GFFs: Draculaura and Viperine Gorgon

Extra-scare-icular activities: Acting (once I've got over my stage fright).

My ghoulfriends say I'm ... a natural onstage and in front of a camera.

Elissabat ™

Age: 17
Fave subject: Biteology – my long-term scareer goal is to work in sports medicine.
Worst subject: Home ick
BFFs: A pack leader never has favourites!

Extra-scare-icular activities:
Football team captain.
My friends say I'm ...
fur-rociously athletic and surprisingly smart.

Clawd Wolf ™

Age: 16 ... in phantom years
Fave subject: Music history – music is my unlife.
Worst subject: Mad science. Sorry Mr Hack, the only thing I wanna create is scary-sweet music!

GFFs: Deuce Gorgon and Holt Hyde
Extra-scare-icular activities: Monster High Music Society member.
My ghoulfriends say I'm ...
the ghoul with the unearthly voice and va-va-voom vintage style.

Operetta ™

Age: 16
Fave subject: Mad science – guess it's in my blood.
Worst subject: Physical dead-ucation, especially when we play dodgeball!
BFFs: Frankie Stein and Deuce Gorgon

Extra-scare-icular activities: Monster High Music Society member.
My friends say I'm ...
crazy-cool (for a normie), although scarily unreliable at times.

Jackson Jekyll ™

Age: 16
Fave subject: Music theory – you don't get to be the beast DJ around by luck!
Worst subject: Everything else

BFFs: I'm down with any monster who digs my beats.
Extra-scare-icular activities: Skultimate Roller Maze.
My friends say I'm ...
a smokin' hot mixer.

Holt Hyde ™

Age: 16
Fave subject: Art, home ick, geometry. I can do all three at the same time and make them all work together.
Worst subject: Dead languages. I basically have to sit on my hands the entire class, which makes me anxious.

GFFs: Ghoulia Yelps and Clawdeen Wolf
Extra-scare-icular activities: I love lending helping hands to my friends by taking their ideas and bringing them to unlife with my illustration and sewing skills.
My ghoulfriends say I'm ... a fan ghoul – it's scary-cool that they trust me with their visions.

Wydowna Spider ™

Age: 15 – though I'm only on the first of my nine lives.
Fave subject: Drama – I can mimic other monsters purr-fectly.
Worst subject: Anything which gets my purrfect paws dirty.
GFFs: Meowlody and Purrsephone

Extra-scare-icular activities: Debate team member. I adore a good argument.
My ghoulfriends say I'm ... a catty kitty who never comes when I'm called.

Toralei Stripe ™

Age: 15
Fave subject: Mad science – especially the module on genetics.
Worst subject: Home ick – Ms Kindergrübber makes us wear full-body hairnets.

GFFs: Meowlody and Toralei
Extra-scare-icular activities: Gymnastics Club – we always land on our feet.
My ghoulfriends say I'm ... purrfectly identical to my sister.

Purrsephone ™

Age: 15
Fave subject: Mad science – especially the module on genetics.
Worst subject: Home ick – Ms Kindergrübber makes us wear full-body hairnets.

GFFs: Purrsephone and Toralei
Extra-scare-icular activities: Gymnastics Club – we always land on our feet.
My ghoulfriends say I'm ... purrfectly identical to my sister.

Meowlody ™

Student Bodies

Age: 15
Fave subject: Li-terror-ture – I love to lose myself in books.
Worst subject: Any class where Mr Zarr is booked as the substitute creature.

GFFs: HooDude Voodoo
Extra-scare-icular activities: Growl Choir member.
My ghoulfriends say I'm ... friendly and wail-y helpful.

Scarah Screams™

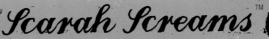

Age: 16
Fave subject: Swimming
Worst subject: Mad science – except when Lagoona and I get paired up for assignments!

BFFs: Deuce Gorgon and Lagoona Blue
Extra-scare-icular activities: Swim team member.
My friends say I'm ... laid-back and sensitive, but an unbeatable monster in the pool!

Gillington 'Gil' Webber™

Age: 16
Fave subject: Music – I'm a keen guitar player.
Worst subject: Any class where I don't get to sit next to a scary-cute ghoul.

BFFs: Clawd Wolf, Deuce Gorgon, Gil Webber
Extra-scare-icular activities: Track team.
My friends say I'm ... the fire and soul of the party!

Heath Burns™

Age: 17
Fave subject: Physical dead-ucation
Worst subject: Music – I can't stand Heath Burns' guitar playing.

BFFs: Gil Webber, Heath Burns. I have a crush on Ghoulia Yelps.
Extra-scare-icular activities: Chess Club member, casketball team member.
My friends say I'm ... deathly slow, but sorta sweet.

Sloman 'Slo Mo' Mortavitch™

Age: Hoo knows? I'm pretty recent, but let's say 15, to make things simple.

Fave subject: Scarecology – I'd like to counsel other monsters.

Worst subject: Volcanology – unsurprising seeing as I'm made of cloth. I'm not a fan of subjects involving fire!

GFFs: Scarah Screams, Frankie Stein

Extra-scare-icular activities: Football team – I'm the tackling target.

My friends say I'm ... a grrrreat listener who can be a horrific pain – due to my voodoo flaw.

HooDude Voodoo™

We don't want to miss any student out of the Monster High Fearbook! Use the space below to add your photo and deets.

Age: 10

Fave subject: Art

Worst subject: Math

GFFs: Ginger praya

Extra-scare-icular activities:

My ghoulfriends say I'm ...

FEARSOME FACULTY

We at Monster High are privileged to have a deadly team of academics helping to fill our skulls with knowledge. These pages are dead-icated to our fearsome faculty members.

Headless Headmistress Bloodgood
Headmistress and Trigular Calcometry 101 Teacher

Credentials:

Sleepy Hollow State B.S. Equestrian Studies
Marie Antoinette AEM M.A. Horticulture/Para-Psychology

Common Bloodgood-isms....

> "Tally-ho Nightmare ... away!"

> "Losing your head is no excuse for not doing the right thing!"

Why we love her....

"Because she is letting me stay while I am doing my studies at the school and am being so very far away from home in the mountains. I think she is good lady."
Abbey Bominable

"She is very nice with animals, which is important for our world."
Venus McFlytrap

"Because she is a great and inspirational role model to the student bodies."
Ghoulia Yelps

Fave Bloodgood moments

"When she let me and the girls have an overnight creepover in the school on Frightday 13th! I got to make Toralei eat furballs 'cause we made it through the night without getting spooked by the beast of coffin corridor. We threw him a totally ughsome party!"
Cleo de Nile

"When she chained me and Abbey together for the day to teach us to get along. It turned out to be a voltageous idea and now we're beast friends."
Frankie Stein

Ms Kindergrübber
Home Ick Teacher

Mr Hackington
Mad Science Teacher

Credentials:
Skinner College B.S. Chemistry
Lancet and Czechit School of Science
M.S. Taxidermy

Why we love him....

"Despite the fact that he loves to cut things up in his class, like poor little frogs - which is never cool - he's not afraid to back down under pressure from sea creatures." Lagoona Blue

Fave 'Hack' moments

"When, like, he turned up with some blood sausages during casketball - that meaty snack helped me win the game!"
Clawd Wolf

"When his 'care for an egg' assignment went horrifically wrong. The egg hatched and attacked Mr H!"
Gil Webber

Common Hack-ism....

"HEATH BURNS!!!!! Do you want to end up in dead-tention for the rest of your life?"

Mr D'eath
Student Guidance Counsellor

Fave Mr D'eath moment

"He let me give him a monster makeover and set him up on a date. Now that's scary-cool!"
Rochelle Goyle

Credentials:
North Styx State B.A. Modern Dance/Journalism
Tombstone Tech M.A. Peace Studies

Why we love him....

"Because he's a little freaky just like us. He's got this 'regret list' where he writes down all the things he plans on regretting before the death of his soul." Frankie Stein

"What's the worst that could happen?"

Common D'eath-ism....

"HE SIGHS A LOT — BUT HE'S ONE FANGTASTICALLY HAPPY DUDE."
Deuce Gorgon

Credentials:
GGT Ghoul Graduate Trainee – retrained after formerly running 'cottage' baking industry and then running a B&B.

Why we love her....

"Because, for some reason she quite likes me - we kinda bond over my stitching." Frankie Stein

"That smells spooktacular Deuce! The rest of you ... back to the chopping board."

Fave Kindergrübber moment

"WHƐN MƐ and FrankiƐ madƐ a living gingƐrbrƐad man in hƐr class. ShƐ lovƐd thƐ big guy!"
Jackson Jekyll

Common Grübb-ism....

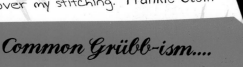

KILLER STYLE QUIZ

Monster High students are never afraid to flaunt their freaky flaws. How better to do it than in a bit of haunt couture? Or some monster designer labels? With or without their Furberry arm candy, the ghouls know eek-xactly how to look their beast. But what's your killer style? Find out which ghoul you're most like by completing this fangtastic quiz.

1

What type of party sounds the ghoulest?

a) A pool party
b) A vamptastic disco
c) A fashion show party

2

What kind of shoes do you most like wearing?

a) Freaky-fab flip-flops
b) Lace-up boots
c) Fur-rocious wedges

3

What's your favourite colour?

a) Ocean blue
b) Hot pink
c) Gore-geous gold

4

What would you love to win in a competition?

a) Some designer swimwear
b) A new iCoffin
c) A shopping spree at the Maul

5 **What's your favourite hairstyle?**

a) Anything that's quick and easy
b) Super-sleek pigtails
c) Big and bouncy, worthy of a shampoo advert!

6 **What kind of accessories do you like best?**

a) Anything fun and quirky
b) Anything heart-shaped
c) Plenty of bling!

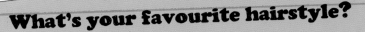

RESULTS!

Mostly Cs:

You're a fierce fashionista, like Clawdeen Wolf™. You love fashion and dressing up, and all things glamorous and ghoul-itzy. You aren't afraid to create your own trends and you dream of owning your own clothing line one day. After that, you'll soon have a whole fashion empire — with everyone watching as you strut your gore-geous stuff. Go, ghoul!

Mostly As:

You're a fresh and natural gill-friend, like Lagoona Blue™. You love the outdoors so usually wear loose, comfortable clothes. That said, you can turn heads in a little black dress when you want to! When it comes to beauty, you like to keep things simple, with a fruit-flavoured lip gloss and the occasional sweep of eyeshadow. Just don't forget to wash that chlorine out of your hair!

Mostly Bs:

You're gore-geously girly, like Draculaura™. You're sweet and kind, and care more about your friends than how you look. You always enjoy a good pampering session and are forever trying to give your ghoulfriends makeovers. You love to wear black with a splash of hot pink, and your favourite accessories are usually fluffy and fangtastic. Scary-cute!

Boo-tiful Treats!

Makeover ghoul Viperine often makes her own freaky-fab make-up products at home. Check out her all-time favourite recipes for boo-ty treatments and try them yourself. Don't forget to check with your creators first, and test the treatments on a teeny patch of skin before using them, just in case you're allergic to any of the ingredients. You don't want a reaction like Abbey gets with pollen … it's not pretty!

SCARYLICIOUS LIP BALM

Find a microwave-safe container and mix half a teaspoon of cocoa powder with four teaspoons of petroleum jelly. Ask a groan-up to put the mixture in the microwave for just a few seconds to warm it up, then pour it into a small jar. Leave your scrummy choco lip balm to cool before using it. Oh, and don't be tempted to eat it – it might smell good enough to spread on your toast, but it's not!

HAIR TO SIGH FOR

Before you head out to a polka-dot disco or ghouls' night out, try this glitzy trick.... Spritz your hair with hairspray, then sprinkle a small amount of loose glitter on top. The glitter will stick to the spray and stay in place as it dries – *voilà!*

MONSTER MASH

Instead of throwing away your old half-empty nail-varnish bottles, mix the varnishes together to make ghoul new shades! Try doing the same thing with half-used lip glosses: mix them well then scrape the mixture into a small container. You'll be the envy of Cleo and score points with Venus at the same time. Frankie calls it a win—win stitch-uation!

PUT A MASK ON IT

Stir 85g of rolled oats and 225g of natural yoghurt together in a bowl. Gently massage the mixture onto your face for two minutes then rinse it off. If your kitchen cupboards look like a graveyard and there are no oats, try natural yoghurt on its own. It makes a fangtastic natural face mask!

THE SKULTIMATE SCRUB

Find a bowl and put in four tablespoons of baby oil, four tablespoons of sea salt and a teaspoon of cocoa powder. Add a few drops of vanilla essence or orange oil, if you have it, and stir everything together. The next time you shower, rub it onto your skin, then rinse it off. Your skin will smell like a scream come true!

Scary-cute Bath Cookies

These bath cookies make voltageous presents for your beasties. Or, if you're a luxury fiend like Cleo, just keep them for yourself! Just remember they are for bathing, not eating! First, make sure you've got a groan-up on alert to help with the hot-oven action.

You will need:

250g salt
75g cornflour
75g baking powder
2 eggs
2 tablespoons of olive oil
Perfume or a drop of scented oil

1. Cover a baking tray with foil and preheat the oven to 180°C.
2. Put all of the ingredients in a bowl and stir them together to make a soft dough.
3. Roll the dough into small balls and press each one onto the foil-covered tray.
4. Put the tray in the oven and bake your cookies for 10 minutes. Use a timer!
5. Remove the tray from the oven and leave the cookies to cool completely.
6. Store your bath cookies in an air-tight container. When you're next having a bath, drop two cookies into the water, let them dissolve and totally relax!

CHART of SHADINESS

Use the Chart of Shadiness to find out which shades work for you! Clawdeen can't stop howling about this ugh-mazing tool. Are you a warm ghoul, like Cleo, or a cool ghoul, like Abbey? The results will help you pick out clothes, accessories and make-up, too.

If your skin is ...

... pale pink or peachy, like Draculaura's

... brown or black, like Catty's

... pale and freckly, like Lagoona's

... olive or honey-toned, like Nefera's™

and your hair is ...

and your hair is ...

	If you're COOL, try these shades:	**If you're WARM, try these shades:**
RED	Raspberry red, scarlet or shocking pink	Salmon, coral pink or tangerine
ORANGE	Light pinkish peach or red-orange	Darker orange and rusty orange
YELLOW	Pale, soft yellow or light, crisp lemon	Mustard yellow, gold or honey yellow
GREEN	Soft mint green or brilliant emerald green	Olive green, khaki or lime
BLUE	Icy pale blue or soft mid-blue	Navy blue, turquoise or bright blue
PURPLE	Lavender, plum or burgundy	Cosy maroon or crisp lilac
NEUTRALS	Cocoa brown or silver grey	Chocolate brown, cream or bronze

... blonde or a light colour, like Viperine's

... black or brown, like Clawdeen's

Your colouring is **COOL**, so you look best in cool shades.

... brown, blonde or red, like Operetta's

... blonde, brown or black, like Cleo's

Your colouring is **WARM**, so you look best in warm shades.

WE'VE GOT SPIRITS HOW BOUT YOU?

27

TRASH to Fash

Even Venus's pollens of persuasion aren't powerful enough to make the whole student body change its ways when it comes to recycling. But with a little help from her skeleton crew, Venus soon oversees Monster High's 'First Annual All-Recycled Completely Renewable Fashion Show'. Don't be a loser, be a reuser, and follow Venus's tips to host your own show!

Find someone with influence to support your show and get people's attention, like Cleo.

Turn old jeans into summer cut-offs!

Don't worry about how you look picking through rubbish. It's for a good cause!

Recycle, reuse and renew! Ghouls look cool while they save the planet.

Swap clothes with friends instead of throwing them away.

Reuse a skinny scarf as a headband or as a belt on your jeans.

Break up a boring necklace and use the beads to make a clawsome chunky bracelet.

Got a boring plain tank-top? Wear it over a T-shirt or dress it up with some badges!

A sparkly brooch collection isn't just for pinning to jackets and bags. Clip one to a plain hairband for glam hair in an instant!

Revamp old or plain hair slides with a couple of coats of nail varnish. Sprinkle some glitter over the final coat before it dries, or press on a few beads, sequins or gems. Totally gore-geous!

Reuse a clawsome pencil case as a make-up bag or scary-cute clutch.

Wear a plant-tastic party dress with thick tights and boots in the winter, or over your jeans to play it casual.

Planet-friendly beauty tips:

Don't buy something just because it's a bargain. If you don't really need it, save your cash – and the planet. You might never wear it and would probably end up throwing it away....

Take a reusable bag to the Maul instead of using plastic carrier bags. It's a genius excuse to buy a new scary-cute bag!

Instead of using conditioner all over your hair, just apply it to the ends. Your freaky-fab locks won't get weighed down, plus your conditioner will last longer, so less rubbish goes to the landfill!

If you have tight curly hair like me, you don't need to wash it often. About once a week is enough – any more than that makes my hair scary dry! Plus, washing it less saves water!

Recycle empty beauty containers by using them to store your creeperific accessories. Then keep them away from sneaking siblings!

Keep your nail varnish in the fridge. It'll last longer, go on more easily and dry quicker, too.

Towel-dry your hair before using a hairdryer. It'll cut down on high-energy blasting time and will be better for your hair, too. If you can leave it to dry completely naturally, even better!

monstrous

MEMORIES

What's your favourite Monster High moment? Here's a collection of our most cherished paw-sonal memories....

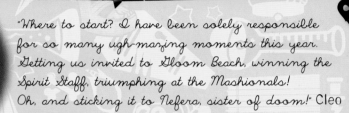

"Where to start? I have been solely responsible for so many ugh-mazing moments this year. Getting us invited to Gloom Beach, winning the Spirit Staff, triumphing at the Mashionals! Oh, and sticking it to Nefera, sister of doom!" Cleo

"It was pretty incredible working with Frankie on our life-sized gingerbread guy for home ick. Doing anything with Frankie is ugh-mazing!"

Jackson

"Rewiring HooDude's brain to give him more confidence. You don't get to do that often!"
Scarah

"I enjoyed the power cut caused by Heath Burns which meant that all technology died at Monster High! For one day I got to show the student bodies how they could exist without their iCoffins, tablets and clawculators!"

Robecca

"I loved working with that fine monster, Deuce, on a song for his ghoulfriend. The chance to write for someone who appreciates my little ol' style of music cancelled out the stress of dealin' with that total pain, Cleo." Operetta

"When Frankie got everyone – including me – tickets to see Justin Biter in concert! She's the beast GFF ever!" Ghoulia

"I remember when the ghouls tried to make me feeling not so much home sick by locking me into freezer. Was very kindness to me. Almost making me to cry." Abbey

"My favourite memory was when the ghouls dressed Slo Mo up as my aunt to attend the Parent-Creature Conference. He looked bonzer! There were no worries anyhow because the teacher just wanted to talk about my excellent grades!" Lagoona

"WATCHING JACKSON JEKYLL CHANGE INTO HOLT HYDE FOR THE FIRST TIME. HILARIOUS! AND GETTING A DATE WITH DRACULAURA, YEAH, THOSE ARE MY TWO TOP MEMORIES THIS YEAR." Heath

"When Clawdeen and Clawd thought that I believed all of Clawdia's stories were true! The whole school knows she's a fur-rociously creative writer!" Howleen

"It was totes amazing when our Gffs planned a surprise joint party for Draculaura and me. It was my Sweet 16 days and her Sweet 1,600 years! We had both been trying to sort out a party for each other, but no one could come, because they were all planning a joint party for us both!" Frankie

"UUUUGGHHG!"

(Ghoulia led our zombie team to victory at dodgeball by using her trigular calcometry skills.) Slo Mo

"When the zombies were fighting over Ghoulia yelps! I've seen paint dry faster!" Holt

"I loved it when Emily Anne came to school for Monster High's "We Stop Hate" campaign. She spread so much love, love, love!" Draculaura

Abbey Bominable's
QUOTES OF THE YEAR

Unlike we mountain-dwelling monsters who are not into the small talk, the Monster High student bodies love to be doing chat together. Here are some of the best sound bites I have heard when fanging out in the howlways.

"I didn't have time to study. I got busy. You think these pores just shrink themselves?"
Draculaura

"Knowledge is the cure for every curse."
Mr Hack

"YOU LOOK HORRIBLE! I LIKE THAT IN A GIRL!"
Heath

"No way am I going out with a guy with more than four eyes ... and he has like, eight!" Frankie

"I nailed the finals like a coffin, sista!"
Clawdeen

"Woah! Slow ya growls."
Clawd

"WHO YOU CALLIN' A BULL?" Manny

"Holt Hyde? No, I don't know him."
Jackson

"Draculaura, you're pretty pumped for somebody without a pulse!" Cleo

"Cleo's been working that cursed idol like a credit card with no limit!" Clawdeen

"MONSTER HIGH'S ABOUT BEING COOL TO EVERYONE NO MATTER WHO OR WHAT YOU ARE, EVEN IF THAT MEANS A 'NORMIE'. Deuce

"It might come back to bite ya!" Lagoona

"If I don't get a scoop soon, I'm just gonna live!" Spectra

"I don't mind when people talk about me. It's when they stop talking about you that you have to worry." Nefera

"I couldn't study for the SATS, my brother ate all my notes." Clawdeen

"I just want to crawl into a puddle and pull it over the top of me!" Lagoona

"She does so much for me I thought I should do something nice for her. But don't tell anyone — it'll totally ruin my rep." Cleo

"Let's just say my clothes aren't the only thing that's fierce during a full moon!" Clawdeen

"I've known Clawd since before he was housebroken." Draculaura

"Y'all are pickin' on the wrong fiddle." Operetta

"UuuughrrrghgghghUgh." Ghoulia

"You are one misdeed away from the study howl of eternal homework – oh, and fiery demons will descend upon your house." Headmistress Bloodgood

"No one is to look directly at me unless it's in amazement." Cleo

"I DON'T GIVE AS!" Mr Rotter

we find out who runs things and we show them who's boss. Then we ghouls will run the school." Toralei

"Voltageous fail! It was like I had death breath." Frankie

"DO YOU BELIEVE IN LOVE AT FIRST FRIGHT? OR SHOULD I WALK BY AGAIN?" Heath

WHAT YOUR ANIMAL DREAMS MEAN

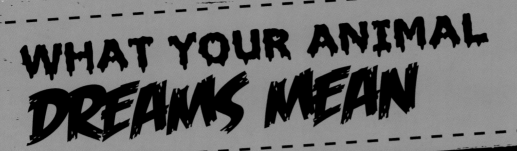

Just a day in the life of a boogey monster.

Twyla loves to capture normie nightmares, so only sweet dreams get through. Want to find out what your creepy-cool animal dreams mean? Twyla has the dream low-down, so read on, ghoulfriend....

CATS

Cats are independent spirits. Dreaming about a cat could be a reminder to be free and not to let anyone or anything hold you back!

DOGS

Dreams about dogs could be a sign that you should follow your intuition. Trust your instincts and go with your gut!

BEES

Buzzing bees in your dreams could mean there's something you really want to say. Perhaps you have a secret you'd desperately like to share with your GFFs!

ELEPHANTS

Elephants usually represent power, and so dreaming about them could mean you're feeling strong and able to handle anything.

BIRDS

If you dream about birds then you might be yearning for freedom. It could be time to make a change and break free!

DOLPHINS

Dreams about dolphins could represent optimism and your willingness to explore and try new things.

FOXES

Foxes are often thought of as cunning and clever. Perhaps you are facing a situation that requires resourcefulness and some discretion!

BATS

Seeing five bats in your dream is unbelievably good luck! They symbolize good health, longevity, peace, wealth and happiness.

PANTHERS

Panthers have power, beauty and grace. So if you dream about them, then chances are you have power, beauty and grace, too!

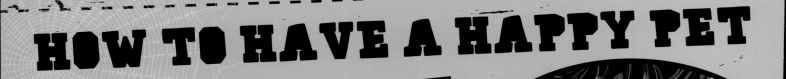

HOW TO HAVE A HAPPY PET

If you have a pet, it's frighteningly important to look after it properly. Jane Boolittle™ has some top tips for looking after animals – and she can speak their language, so her advice is totally clawsome!

FOOD

Just like their owners, pets need food for energy and to keep them fur-bulously fit and healthy. Good grub will also help to keep your pet's fangs, claws and coat in tip-top condition. If you're unsure what sort of food is best for your creature, visit the vet for some expert advice. Remember, different types of creature need different types of food! For example, some animals like meat and others are veggies.

DRINK

Having lots of fresh water to drink is also essential for most animals. So to be an aqua-some owner, always keep an eye on your pet's water bowl and make sure it's topped up regularly. Being dehydrated is so not cool!

36

GROOMING

Even animals can have bad scare days! So brush your pet's coat often to keep it untangled and looking fangtastic. While you're doing this, check for little bitey bugs that might be hiding in there and annoying your pet. Sometimes they will also need a bath. Good luck with that – lots of creatures hate getting wet so you will have a splashing time!

EXERCISE

Physical dead-ucation might not be your favourite subject, but some pets need plenty of playtime and exercise. They have lots of energy that they need to use up! Taking walks together is fun and will be good exercise for you, too – so get outside, run around and feel the wind in your fur. You could even play a game of Hide and Shriek with your pet!

LOVE

Pets have feelings, too, even pets made of stone like Rockseena and Roux, the gargoyle animals. So show your companion creature some love and affection, and of corpse you'll get it back tenfold in return!

your pet DeStiNy

Spectra is spookily curious to find out what type of animal would be your purr-fect pet. She's set some questions on her blog, 'The Ghost Post' – answer them to reveal your pet destiny and then she'll spread the word!

1. How much free time do you have each week?
A) A few hours, in between fearleading and revising in study howl or the li-bury.
B) A good amount. You're usually pretty free on the weekends when school's out.
C) Not much. You're always fanging out with ghoulfriends, shopping at the Maul and throwing fangtastic parties.

2. What's your scream date?
A) Dinner at a killer new restaurant.
B) An aqua-some day playing at the beach.
C) Seeing a frighteningly good movie.

3. When it comes to ghouls dressing their pets, you think:
A) Kinda over it!
B) Makes you furr-ious.
C) It's the ghoulest!

4. You would name your animal after:
A) A pop star, such as Justin Biter or a monster from One Dissection.
B) Your GFF.
C) A fashion designer, like Jean Maul Ghostier or Alexander McScream.

5. Your friends would say you're:
A) A social ghoul.
B) Totally chilled.
C) A freaky-fab trendsetter.

6. After school, you can most likely be found:
A) At fearleading practice.
B) At the li-bury.
C) Shopping with your ghoulfriends at the Maul.

7. You want a pet that will:
A) Be easy to take care of.
B) Have fun with you when your GFF's not around.
C) Attract attention.

8. The website you can't live without is:
A) FrightTube
B) Monsterpedia
C) Critter

Results:

MOSTLY As:

You should get a playful puppy like Frankie or a scary-cute kitten like Clawdeen! Anything can be fun if you have the right attitude, and you always do! People love to spend time with you because you're always smiling and enjoying yourself. You like to chat, play and let loose and a puppy or kitten would keep pace with your on-the-go unlife!

MOSTLY Bs:

You should get a freaky-fab fish like Lagoona or a plant like Venus! You've got scary-cool style, love to take it easy and care deeply about the environment. You enjoy unlife at a leisurely pace. Taking care of most fish and plants is easy! While you're chilling out on the couch, your companion creature can swim or sit nearby.

MOSTLY Cs:

You should get an exotic snake like Cleo or a spider like Operetta! When you walk into school, people notice. You always look fangtastic and like to be the centre of attention – you can't help that you were created drop-dead gore-geous! A pet snake or a spider is a little showy, but wouldn't mess with your busy unlifestyle.

The Paw-fect

I am suggesting that all student bodies find a study buddy with whom to exchange knowledge. Try my logical and geometrical diagram to help you find the paw-fect partner with whom to work. Good luck.

Who's your ultimate homework fiend? Answer each question, then follow the arrows to find your scarylicious study buddy.

My pencil case is always freaky-fabulous!

YES

NO

Of course I'll study ... after fearleading!

YES

NO

YES

NO

Hiss-tory is the best subject on the scare-iculum.

YES

NO

YES

Frankie Stein

Freaky-fab minds think alike and Frankie is one enthusiastic study buddy! When you've finished comparing scary-cool stationery, you'll get straight down to work on your hiss-tory or home ick assignments.

Cleo de Nile

Your working partnership with Cleo is sure to be golden. You'd both rather be fearleading than studying, but you'll happily swot up on geometry over a spookaccino at the Coffin Bean!

Draculaura

Even books need makeovers sometimes and, like Draculaura, you spend almost as much time on presentation as content, covering textbooks in fierce paper and highlighting passages in hot-pink pen.

40

Study Buddy

START

Learning is much fiercer with a study buddy.

YES → I'd rather study at the Coffin Bean.

NO → The li-bury is the beast place to work!

I love scary-cool highlighter pens in ice-blue or pink.

YES — **NO** → I'd just die if my grades slipped!

Talking work through with ghoulfriends helps me revise.

YES — **NO** → When it comes to learning, I'm a high-tech kinda ghoul. ← **YES** — **NO**

YES ↓ **NO** →

Abbey Bominable

You and Abbey are ghouls of few words, preferring to read and write rather than discuss and recite lessons. You are both logical creatures who shine at maths and are top of Mr Mummy's class.

Ghoula Yelps

An ogre-achiever like you should definitely buddy up with Ghoulia. Just like the clever zombie you're happiest reading tomes in the li-bury or researching your next assignment on Boo-gle.

Robecca Steam

You like to work the traditional way and would rather handwrite homework with a quill than use a computer. This is long-winded, but as Robecca always says, "Less monster haste – more spooky speed!"

Scarah's Quiz

Scarah Screams can read your mind but not your future! Try her scareers quiz instead. Circle your answers then add up your points to discover your result.

1. I fangsolutely adore drawing, painting and arty activities.
Agree (5)   Sort of agree (3)   Disagree (1)

2. Mad science is one of my beast subjects.
Agree (1)   Sort of agree (3)   Disagree (5)

3. I'm a total drama queen!
Agree (5)   Sort of agree (3)   Disagree (1)

4. I'm squealy good at maths.
Agree (1)   Sort of agree (3)   Disagree (5)

5. I like reading all kinds of li-terror-ture.
Agree (5)   Sort of agree (3)   Disagree (1)

6. I'd love to go to Monster High so I could study astronomy.
Agree (1)   Sort of agree (3)   Disagree (5)

7. It would be ugh-mazing to study volcanoes in volcanology.
Agree (1)   Sort of agree (3)   Disagree (5)

8. I think I'd be good at dead languages.
Agree (5)   Sort of agree (3)   Disagree (1)

9. Monster anatomy sounds gory and fun!
Agree (1)   Sort of agree (3)   Disagree (5)

10. I wish we had cinemat-ogre-phy at my school.
Agree (5)   Sort of agree (3)   Disagree (1)

10-24:

Have you thought about becoming a doctor? Or, if biteology makes you feel queasy, perhaps think about becoming an astronaut, or a pilot ... so many options!

25-35:

You like a good mix of subjects and might often change your mind about your future job. Don't worry – just keep doing whatever it is you enjoy most and the future will figure itself out!

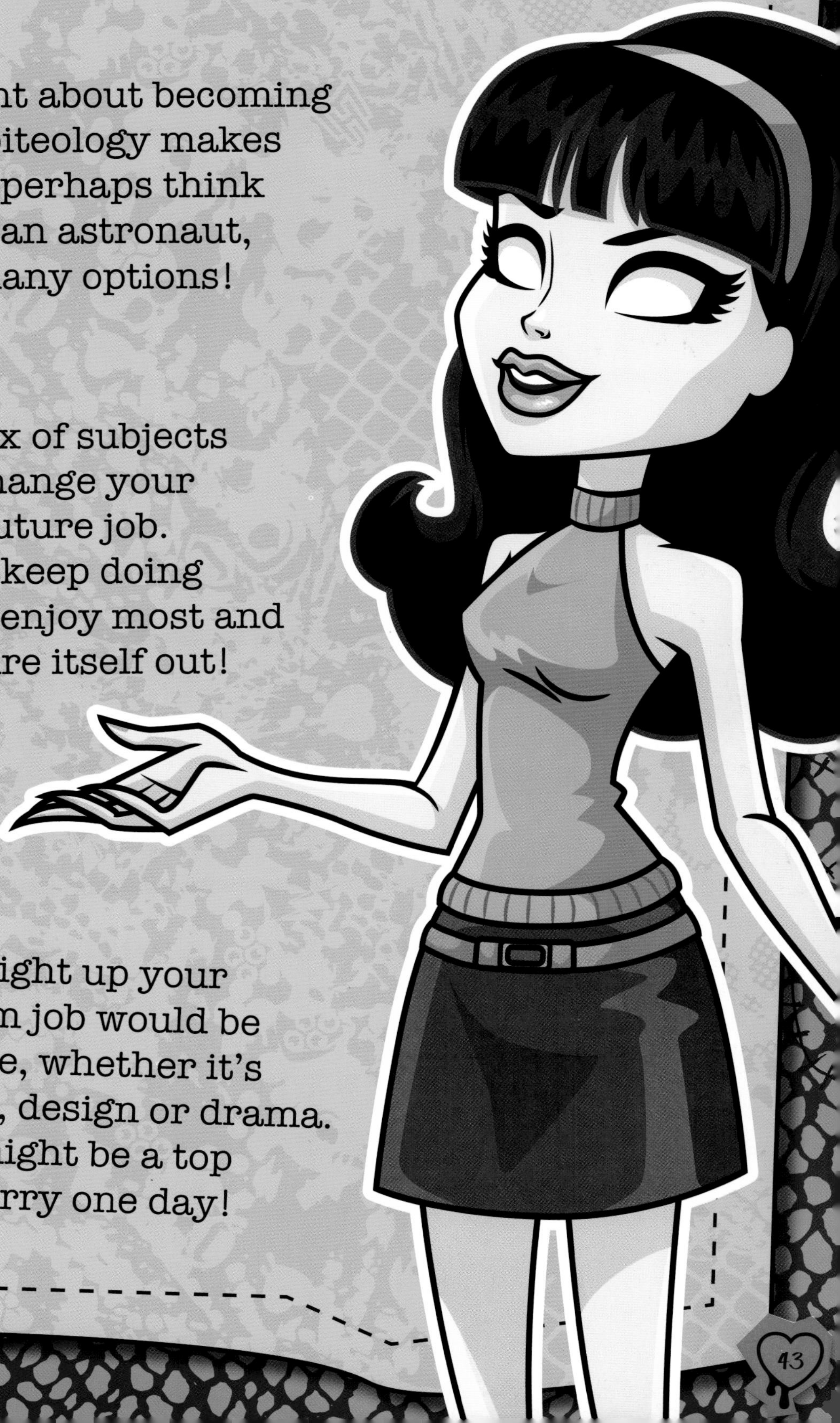

36-50:

Anything arty is right up your street! Your dream job would be something creative, whether it's with words, music, design or drama. Who knows, you might be a top designer for Furberry one day!

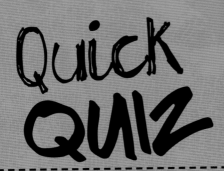

Quick QUIZ

What part do you usually play in a group? Are you a clawsome leader, the paw-fect wing-ghoul or a terror-ific team player? Answer these questions to find out!

You accidentally walk into a debate team meeting. Do you:
- 💜 apologize for interrupting and walk away?
- 💎 take a seat and quietly listen to everyone?
- ⚡ quickly join in and enjoy the debate?

Cleo's holding auditions for a new Fear Squad member. Do you:
- ⚡ turn up and start suggesting new dance moves?
- 💜 keep well away? (The Fear Squad is not for you!)
- 💎 go along, despite feeling nervous?

Bloodgood asks you to organize an end-of-scaremester party. Do you:
- 💎 agree to help, but only if no one else wants to do it?
- ⚡ immediately agree? (How eek-citing!)
- 💜 politely decline and suggest someone else does it?

Clawdeen's catwalk show is a mess behind the scenes! Do you:
- ⚡ quickly get everyone under control?
- 💜 find Clawdeen and ask how to help?
- 💎 start quietly tidying up on your own?

Ghoulia wants to set up a study group but needs a translator. Do you:
- 💎 help set up a study timetable then tell everyone about it?
- 💜 advertise the group by putting up posters?
- ⚡ offer to run it instead?

44

MOSTLY ⚡

Like Cleo, you love being the leader of the group. You're able to make difficult choices when you need to. Your ghoulfriends probably look to you when they need a decision made.

MOSTLY 💎

Like Ghoulia, you're good at solving problems and are often the brains of the group. Sometimes you don't like it when plans are changed at the last minute, but you're happy to step in and take charge.

MOSTLY 💜

You're a fangtastic team player, like Draculaura. You're always willing to lend a hand and everyone loves you for it. You can be shy at times, but your friends are always keen to hear what you have to say.

PICTURE DAY PICK

Picture Day is one of the most important events in the Monster High school calendar! Each student's monstrous image is preserved for eternity (and even shown in the Fearbook), so you need to look your absolute beast. Answer YES or NO to the first question, then follow the arrows through the chart to discover whose scary-cool style you'd pick to pose in.

START

I always put on my spookiest smile for the camera.

I like to check my freaky reflection before I pose.

YES → I love electrifying patterns and prints.

YES

NO

NO

In a gruesome group shot, I make sure I'm at the front.

A golden ghoul like me always flings on the bling.

NO → I look fierce in frills.

NO

YES

YES → I look creepily chic in mini-dresses.

YES

My killer style features lots of fitted pieces.

NO → Halter neck styles look clawsome on me.

YES

NO

Plaid detail shoes are frightfully pretty

YES

I might wear shocking stockings or tights.

YES

YES

Shoes? Hmm ... monstrous metallics are my fave.

NO

NO → Any killer heel rules as long as it's black or pink.

YES

A semi-up hair-do looks hairrific.

YES

You wear high-voltage heels and spooky separates to mix up a freaky-unique style that's all your own. Ughsome accessories are your thing — you know how to wear a scary-cute bag, horrific hat or beastly braces to set off your outfit. You're one fierce fashionista whose stand-out style means you always shine in the shot.

NO

YES

I'm freakily unique in quirky accessories like braces.

YES

NO

You'd die for Frankie's voltageous fashion flair!

NO

I like shoe straps that snake eerily round my ankles.

Your spooky sweet smile looks great in photos and your colour of choice — shocking pink — always makes an impact. For a freaky photo session you match monstrous make-up with a pair of killer heels. Dresses with fierce frills make you feel gorgeously ghoul-ie.

NO

YES

Scary-cute bunches work for me.

You think Draculaura's look is fangtastic!

YES

NO

My hair looks spooktacular worn long with a fringe.

You know the creepy camera loves you and you're confident that you always look ugh-mazing. For your close-up you'll be wearing something fitted to show off your fearsome figure. You like wearing your hair lusciously long and spooktacularly sleek.

NO

YES

You admire Cleo's killer style!

PAGES 49-80

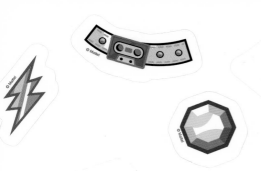

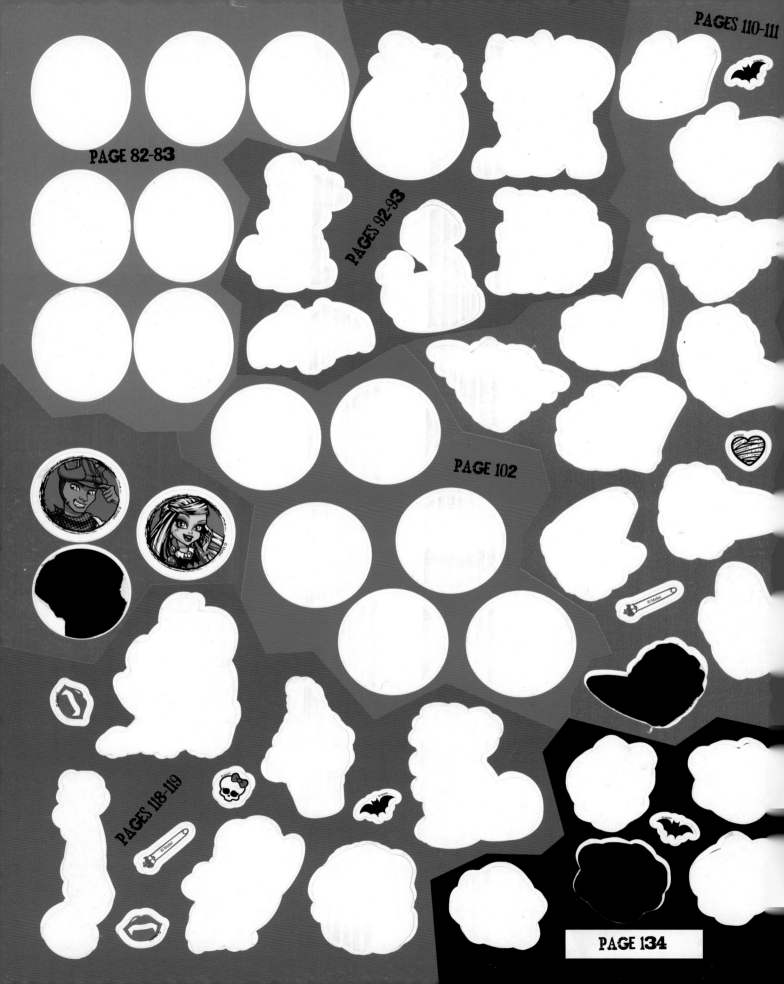

PAGES 110-111

PAGE 82-83

PAGES 92-93

PAGE 102

PAGES 118-119

PAGE 134

TRUE

TRUE

TRUE

TRUE

TRUE

PAGE 152

PAGE 162

PAGE 135

PAGE 173

MONSTER HIGH

MONSTER STICKER dressing

SPOOKY STYLES

The ghouls and guys at Monster High have cool control of their unique killer style. **Clawdeen Wolf** makes monsters howl with her fierce animal prints and **Frankie Stein's** electrifying style is totally voltage! Learn more about the monsters' freaky-fab fashion sense, then dress them in ugh-mazing outfits. You can style each monster more than once, so get creepy and get creative!

USE YOUR SCARY-COOL STICKERS AND CREEPIEST COLOURING PENS TO DRESS THE MONSTERS.

Draculaura
loves to splash her black outfits with pink.

She carries a frilly umbrella to protect her vampire skin from the sun!

Cleo de Nile is a true ancient Egyptian princess complete with bandages.

She always wears golden jewellery and is rarely seen without her iCoffin.

Frankie Stein
always chooses electrifying patterned prints.

She accessorizes spookily well.

Ghoulia Yelps
is never without a pair of geek-chic glasses.

She thinks the colour red is to die (again) for!

Clawdeen Wolf
howls for anything purple.

She wears a wild green wig for monster parties!

SPOOKY STYLES

Lagoona Blue likes to creep out in her baggies, tank-top and floppies.

She adds scary sparkle with her shell jewellery.

He wears scary-cool shorts and a vest for sports.

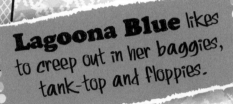

52

Of corpse **Cleo** always looks perfect.

Draculaura has no reflection — she relies on her ghoulfriends to tell her she looks fangtastic!

Lagoona's favourite colour is ocean blue.

Frankie loves to accessorize with an electrifying tie.

Ghoulia loves to lurch around in blood-red clothes.

Animal prints make **Clawdeen** howl!

This ancient Egyptian princess looks ghoulish in gold.

Deuce keeps it creepily casual when he's shooting some hoops.

This romantic vampire loves to accessorize with lace and hearts.

Lagoona likes to dress for any kind of scary fun, like beach volleyball!

Tartan patterns make
Frankie's bolts spark!

Being ghoulishly geeky is part of **Ghoulia's** scary-cool style.

Clawdeen's confidence makes her a fierce fashionista.

Cleo wouldn't be seen undead without royal jewellery to match her outfit.

Deuce mixes black, white and grey with bright colours that rock!

Draculaura is 1,600 years young, so she's had plenty of time to perfect her killer style.

Lagoona loves to dress up in a little black dress for monster parties.

Even when **Frankie** comes apart at the seams, her style stays perfectly in place.

Ghoulia's horn-rimmed glasses match every outfit!

Clawdeen loves purple and gold as a creeperific combination.

Cleo is technically over 5,800 years old. If she didn't wear bandages, her age would start to show!

Deuce designs his own shoes with deadly cool details.

This vegetarian vamp adds sweet details with dots and stripes.

This stylish sea monster loves to use hints of light pink that look sweet against her blue skin.

Frankie sticks to a classic look, but gives it a terrifying twist!

Ghoulia loves freaky-fab T-shirts with zombie comic-book heroes on them.

This wildly stylish ghoul plans to start her own fierce fashion label.

Turquoise and ghoulish gold are **Cleo's** favourite colours.

UGHSOME aCTiViTIES

The MONSTER HIGH fearBook

It's that time of year!
The Monster High
Fearbook has been
created and the awards
have been decided.
But the winners'
pictures are missing!
Add the correct
monster sticker next
to each award.

MOST LIKELY TO ...

... be an A-list star of stage and scream.

MOST LIKELY TO ...

... help out a ghoulfriend in need.

MOST LIKELY TO ...

... fly off into the sunset with the monster of her nightmares.

MOST LIKELY TO ...

... design a fur-rocious pair of killer heels.

MOST LIKELY TO ...

... go on a fangtastic round-the-world trip.

MOST LIKELY TO ...

... be the next spookily smart headmistress of Monster High.

MOST LIKELY TO ...

... become a Skultimate Roller Maze commentator.

83

Tween Esteem

Everyone is totally freaked when they hear that celeb blogger Grimmily Anne™ is visiting Monster High. She runs the world-famous WeStopHate campaign! These entries have been pulled from random students' diaries. Can you guess who wrote each one?

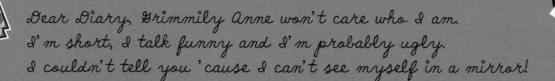

1 *Dear Diary, Grimmily Anne won't care who I am. I'm short, I talk funny and I'm probably ugly. I couldn't tell you 'cause I can't see myself in a mirror!*

2 Heath told me I'm not a real dude and he's right. I'll never be real. Sometimes I can't help but hate myself.

3 Grimmily Anne is high voltage! Maybe she can give me some advice. Most of the time, I'm pretty happy with how I look, but sometimes I feel I need to impress my friends.

4 I know exactly what to wear and how to wear it, but my hair grows super fast. I hate all the plucking and shaving I have to do! Sometimes it's hard work being me, but I have to look my absolute beast for Grimmily Anne!

5 Golly, I'd love to meet Miss Grimmily Anne! She's a super star! I just hope I don't make a darn fool outta myself.

6 *Of course Grimmily Anne will want to meet me! I am of the utmost importance at Monster High. As for flaws, what flaws?*

Clawdeen Wolf Draculaura Operetta™ HooDude Voodoo™ C'leo de Nile™ Frankie Stein

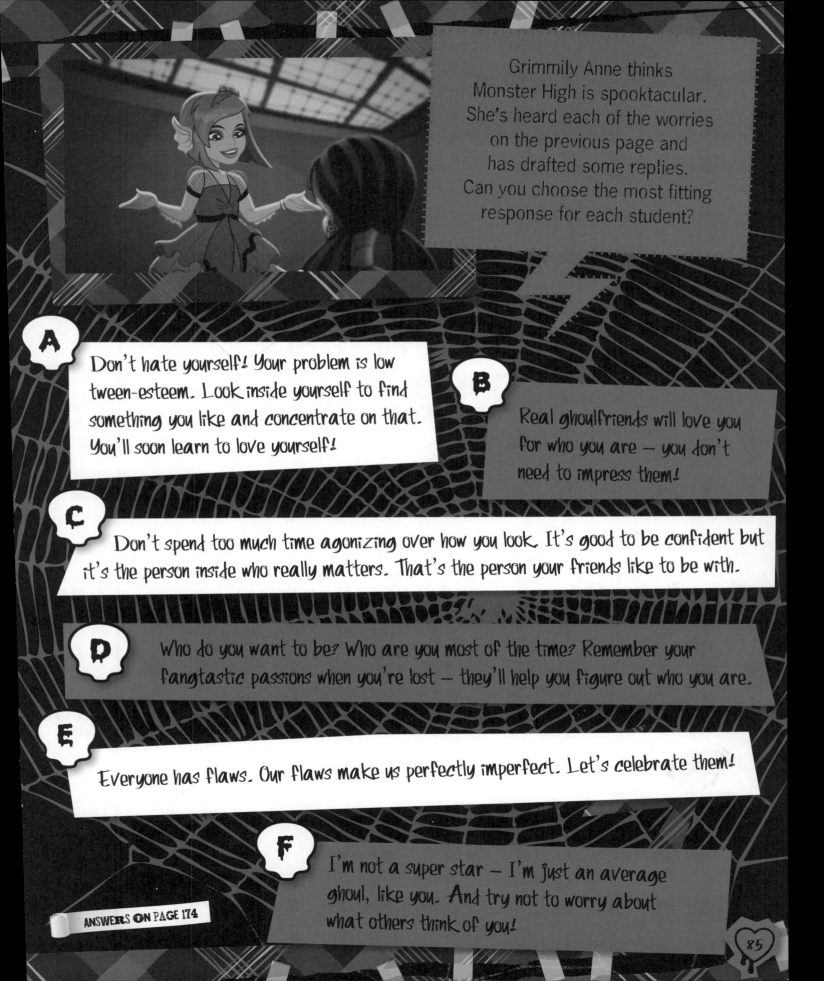

Grimmily Anne thinks Monster High is spooktacular. She's heard each of the worries on the previous page and has drafted some replies. Can you choose the most fitting response for each student?

A Don't hate yourself! Your problem is low tween-esteem. Look inside yourself to find something you like and concentrate on that. You'll soon learn to love yourself!

B Real ghoulfriends will love you for who you are — you don't need to impress them!

C Don't spend too much time agonizing over how you look. It's good to be confident but it's the person inside who really matters. That's the person your friends like to be with.

D Who do you want to be? Who are you most of the time? Remember your fangtastic passions when you're lost — they'll help you figure out who you are.

E Everyone has flaws. Our flaws make us perfectly imperfect. Let's celebrate them!

F I'm not a super star — I'm just an average ghoul, like you. And try not to worry about what others think of you!

ANSWERS ON PAGE 174

Fashionably FIERCE

It's Fashion Week at Monster High! Each ghoul has come up with her own freaky-fab fashion-show theme with a new collection to model. The ghouls can't wait to see their ughsome designs being modelled on the catwalk! Headless Headmistress Bloodgood has even invited the monster-razzi. Can you match each ghoul with the unique fashion-show theme she came up with?

1. GREEN IS THE NEW BLACK

2. Pretty in Pink

3. WALK LIKE AN EGYPTIAN

4. VOLTAGEOUS VOGUE

5. Geek Chic

6. ICE-COOL COUTURE

7. POP STAR POWER

8. WEREWOLVES IN WEDGES

Catty Draculaura Cleo Venus Ghoulia Abbey Clawdeen Frankie

Choose one of the ghouls' scare-raising themes (or come up with your own) and design a poster for the spooktacular show. Who will be the face of your fierce new collection? What are the hottest pieces? Include all the dead-cool deets!

Clawsome *Colours*

The Monster High skeleton crew oozes confidence when it comes to knowing which colours work for them. Their favourite colours are listed below and hidden in the wordsearch – forwards, backwards, up and down. Can you find them all?

B	H	N	I	L	E	B	L	U	E	Y	R	B	L	Z
Z	M	C	R	F	N	E	E	R	G	N	O	E	N	R
L	A	L	R	H	K	G	N	U	D	J	Y	S	H	S
B	R	F	H	D	D	K	S	N	K	D	A	D	H	D
R	I	C	E	B	L	U	E	R	B	K	L	M	N	F
G	G	Z	S	P	O	M	A	V	A	R	R	M	B	D
J	O	S	G	S	G	P	U	R	P	L	E	E	L	N
D	L	H	D	T	D	V	A	A	K	A	D	M	U	E
U	D	K	S	H	S	B	S	J	A	K	A	T	R	T
S	J	S	K	W	F	G	P	I	N	K	L	M	P	P
P	A	H	D	O	C	E	A	N	B	L	U	E	L	N
B	T	E	A	L	R	S	T	W	Y	I	A	H	E	R
A	J	A	H	L	H	D	F	D	T	N	E	E	R	G
T	M	A	G	E	N	T	A	H	T	U	J	O	K	H
G	H	Y	B	Y	H	S	I	D	R	B	V	U	A	S

ANSWERS ON PAGE 174

teal • nile blue • gold • yellow • pink • neon green • ocean blue • green

ice blue • blurple • royal red • marigold • purple • magenta

88

Do you know which student chose which colour in the wordsearch?
Fill in the missing letters below to complete the names of the colours.

CATTY NOIR™
_AG_ _ _A

SLO MO™
P_ _P_ _

JINAFIRE LONG™
R_Y_ _ _ _E_

LAGOONA BLUE
O_ _A_ _L_ _

DEUCE GORGON™
_ _ON_R_ _N

SCARAH SCREAMS™
G_ _ _E_

NEFERA DE NILE™
N_I_ _B_ _ _ _

JACKSON JEKYLL™
Y_ _ _ _W

TWYLA™
BL_ _ _PL_ _

CLEO DE NILE
_ _ _L_ _

ABBEY BOMINABLE™
_C_ _B_ _ _E

CLAWD WOLF™
T_ _ _

DRACULAURA
_ _ _K

SKELITA CALAVERAS™
_ _AR_ _ _L

ANSWERS ON PAGE 174

HAIR-RIFIC!

It's do or dye at Monster High, where everyone's free to wear their hair how they want. Deuce rocks a snake-hawk while Viperine causes hiss-teria with her slithering locks. Try out some new colours on these ghouls, giving them some stunning stripes to get heads turning in the corridors. Frankie wants to brighten up her black and white locks with some highlights, while Draculaura has given strict instructions that she still wants some pink on show!

Next, try out some electrifying make-up colours on the ghouls' faces. Cleo has requested that you makeover the others first, so your technique is perfected before you're let loose on her highly superior bone structure....

FREAKY PETS

All the Monster High students have ugh-mazing monster pets. Find the stickers that match the blank shapes to reunite the ghouls with their beast friends.

COUNT FABULOUS

They love fanging out together!

WATZIT

Stitched together and scary cute!

CRESCENT

Fur-rociously fuzzy and totally clawsome.

ANSWERS ON PAGE 174

HISSETTE

Her hiss is worse than her bite.

NEPTUNA

A fangtastic fishy friend.

SIR HOOTS A LOT

A wise companion, but he doesn't do errands.

93

My SPOOKY Scare-itage

This is Mr Rotter's classroom. Check out the 'My Spooky Scare-itage' project his students are working on. Fang-scinating stuff! Some of the ghouls haven't quite finished. Shall we lend them a claw?

Be a good ghoulfriend and help the students complete their assignments on time. Read each piece of work, then fill in the blanks. All of the words you need are jumbled up in the panel opposite.

My Spooky Scare-itage

NAME: Skelita ....
DEAD-SCENDED FROM: Los Eskeletos
SCARY-COOL COUNTRY: ....
MY SCARE-ITAGE: I am very proud of my scare-itage and its legends and traditions. My favourite custom is Día de los .... (or Day of the Dead), where we honour our ancestors. We spend time with la familia, hold parties and decorate our homes with marigold flowers and screamily scrummy sugar skulls.

My Spooky Scare-itage

NAME: .... Long
DEAD-SCENDED FROM: Chinese ....
SCARY-COOL COUNTRY: China
MY SCARE-ITAGE: The country of my fore-monsters is very eek-xotic, with customs and traditions that have carried on for thousands and thousands of years. Monsters like me were often found guarding temples. We have always had great powers and can control elements including ...., wind and water.

My Spooky Scare-itage

NAME: Cleo ...... Nile

DEAD-SCENDED FROM: ....

SCARY-COOL COUNTRY: ....

MY SCARE-ITAGE: My father tells me that, traditionally, monsters like me were entombed in pyramids in the middle of the desert with .... and gold and sooo much bling. We still live in my father's pyramid and I have my own totes amazing crypt! Our bodies were wrapped in an OTT amount of bandages – the updated version of this look we now call 'bodycon'.

MY SPOOKY SCARE-ITAGE

NAME: ....

DEAD-SCENDED FROM: The Gargoyles

SCARY-COOL CITY: ....

MY SCARE-ITAGE: Stone is a big part of my culture. My ancestors have always been found on and around great ...., such as castles and cathedrals, which we protect. Although I come from Scaris, monsters like me are found in many countries, including ancient Egypt and Greece. We can take many forms.

THE MUMMY   SCARIS   HEXICO   JINAFIRE   FIRE

DRAGONS   DE   MUERTOS   CALAVERAS

BUILDINGS   JEWELS   EGYPT   ROCHELLE GOYLE

MY SPOOKY SCARE-ITAGE

Complete your own assignment here!

NAME: ....

DEAD-SCENDED FROM: ....

SCARY-COOL COUNTRY: ....

MY SCARE-ITAGE: ....

Ghoul-dilocks

ANSWERS ON PAGE 174

Honey Swamp™ can't find her precious camera! Some body or other borrowed it while she was in cinemat-ogre-phy class. Since then, they've been floating around Monster High, snapping sneaky shots of ghouls' hair! Can you identify the ghouls from these scarylicious snapshots? Write their names beneath their photos.

Dressed for THRILLS!

All the guys and ghouls at Monster High have a totally individual killer style. Unscramble the words below to reveal the names of some particularly voltageous looks, then match each one with the student body who rocks it.

1. TANGYPIE SPINCERS

2. WEPUKNRE

3. HOOB

4. TRILAB PEPR

5. RIPBELTS

6. FPYLOP SALACU

7. LEGJUN HICC

8. TRAPY ACICH

9. CORK N LORL KEEG

10. GOULARM SUPS

1. _ _ _ _ _ _ _ _   _ _ _ _ _ _ _ _

2. _ _ _ _ _ _ _ _

3. _ _ _ _

4. _ _ _ _ _ _   _ _ _ _

5. _ _ _ _ _ _ _ _

6. _ _ _ _ _ _   _ _ _ _ _

7. _ _ _ _ _ _   _ _ _ _

8. _ _ _ _ _   _ _ _ _ _

9. _ _ _ _   'N'   _ _ _ _   _ _ _ _

10. _ _ _ _ _ _ _   _ _ _ _

HooDude Voodoo

Cleo de Nile

Catty Noir

Invisi Billy™

Jane Boolittle

Viperine Gorgon™

Skelita Calaveras

Wydowna Spider™

Howleen Wolf™

Clawdia Wolf™

EGYPTIAN PRINCESS • ROCK 'N' ROLL GEEK

PARTY CHICA • BLIPSTER • FLOPPY CASUAL

TRIBAL PREP • WEREPUNK • BOHO

GLAMOUR PUSS • JUNGLE CHIC

ANSWERS ON PAGE 174

97

MONSTER Quiz

Forget about that Scary Aptitude Test for a moment and test your ghoul genius instead with this monster fashion and beauty quiz. Tick true or false for each statement.

	TRUE	FALSE
1. Clawdeen competes for the chance to be an apprentice for fashion designer Bouis Buibbon.	☐	☐
2. Elissabat can often be found on tween movie sets in Hauntlywood.	☐	☐
3. Cleo teaches Operetta to be a lady in order to meet her heroine, Crescenda von Hammerstone.	☐	☐
4. Heath is the perfect model for the scare-itage art show students.	☐	☐
5. Draculaura always keeps her locker in perfect order, just like her make-up bag.	☐	☐
6. Catty Noir likes to wear things that sparkle and flash because they make her feel lucky.	☐	☐
7. Cleo's amulets always do exactly what she wants them to do.	☐	☐
8. Slo Mo beat Cleo to her favourite store at the Maul when the new autumn collection arrived.	☐	☐
9. Ghoulbana and Ghoulace are favourite designer labels among the student bodies.	☐	☐
10. The ghouls once convinced Nefera that it was okay to carry a dead rat instead of a handbag.	☐	☐
11. Abbey uses a youth potion from her grand-mummy to audition for *The Wizard of Ooze*.	☐	☐
12. Clawd gets Draculaura a bracelet but Frankie knocks it into the deep end of the pool.	☐	☐

	TRUE	FALSE
13. Heath Burns thinks he's a bit of a trendsetter among the guys at Monster High.	☐	☐
14. Gil Webber feels at home wearing shorts and flip-flops.	☐	☐
15. Clawd never takes fashion advice from his sister, Clawdeen.	☐	☐
16. Twyla's favourite colour is purblue, a mixture of blue and purple.	☐	☐
17. Skelita Calaveras is always dressed to party because that's what unlife is – one giant party!	☐	☐
18. Jinafire Long says it's easy to find haunt couture fashions that accommodate her dragon's tail.	☐	☐
19. Howleen Wolf loves to mash styles together. It doesn't always work, but she doesn't care!	☐	☐
20. Viperine is often known as the 'makeover ghoul'. She loves experimenting with make-up.	☐	☐

Now check your answers on page 174 and turn back to see how you did.

1-6 POINTS:

Okay, so your olds aren't going to under-ground you for doing badly on a fashion and beauty quiz but still, you have some serious homework to do, ghoul! Start by borrowing a few copies of *Teen Scream* from Frankie or another tween magazine that tickles your fancy. Then get your ghoulfriends to test you on the freaky facts.

7-15 POINTS:

Not totally shocking but not ugh-mazing either. Pay more attention to the Monster High ghouls and you'll soon be up there at the top of the perfectly imperfect fashion stakes! If that's not where you want to be, that's fine too. Just be happy and flaunt those flaws, ghoulfriend!

16-20 POINTS:

Oh. My. Ra. Cleo has some serious competition on her bandage-wrapped hands! Get down to the Maul right now and reward yourself with a little freaky treat. Just beware not to spend too much time floating around the shops – we don't want your schoolwork to fall behind or you'll have Headmistress Bloodgood on your back!

99

Spooktacular Style

The students are busy writing their profiles for the Monster High Fearbook but the deadline is looming! Yikes! Can you help them? Read each piece, then use the words in the panel to fill in the blanks.

swamp   palette   Ageless
Clawdia   tribal   Scaris
make-up   mixing   earrings
scaredrobe   gold   sisters
purple   colour   Veronica
home   manicure   dresses

NAME: Catrine de Mew™

AGE: 17

LOVES: _____, bien sûr!

KILLER STYLE: I prefur to attract the monster tourist with my art instead of my fashion as it is more important. *Mais j'adore* all things Scarisian! The accessories, the bags, the scarves – they are all *très, très jolie!* Today my favourite _____ , it is lavender but tomorrow, *qui sait?* There are so many colours inside the _____ .

NAME: Honey Swamp

AGE: 115 in _____ monster years

LOVES: Green and yellow

KILLER STYLE: Others might say I'm ghouly and sweet in appearance. My _____ is filled with freakily feminine prints, skirts and _____ . My perfectionist ways mean you can't rush me at anything – and that includes getting ready!

ANSWERS ON PAGE 174

NAME: Nefera de Nile

AGE: _____ , of course!

LOVES: Getting Cleo to do my shopping for me. That's what little _____ are for!

KILLER STYLE: I go for fashions and accessories that accentuate my timeless beauty. Anything _____ totally rocks my tomb because it doesn't tarnish or rust, much like myself. But if I can't have gold (and why can't I?) then Nile blue is the next best thing. It's a constant reminder of my eternal beauty.

NAME: _____ Wolf

AGE: 19

LOVES: Londoom – it's totally undead with fashion and literary history.

KILLER STYLE: I like to mix graphic _____ prints with a preppy style to create a sort of 'tribal prep' look. It's totally me! I'm not good with manicures though. One year, Clawdeen got me a _____ for my birthday but on the way home I got an idea for a story and had a bit of a chew.... Little sis was not happy!

NAME: Elissabat a.k.a. _____ Von Vamp™

AGE: 1601

LOVES: Lace, ruffles, satin and silk

KILLER STYLE: I'll wear anything frilly, as long as it's black or _____ . I fangsolutely love my dangly _____ and knee-high boots, too. I guess being an actress means I get to try loads of different costumes so that off-scream, I know exactly what suits me and what doesn't. Yep, it's pretty scary-cool!

NAME: Viperine Gorgon

AGE: 17

LOVES: Shimmery things

KILLER STYLE: I don't sssscale back when it comes to _____ different colours, patterns and fabricssss. Shopping for _____ is one of my favourite things to do and sometimes I even go to the elder monsters' _____ and do makeovers for the monsters there. I get to hear some ughsome stories!

SCARY-COOL SEQUENCES

GHOULIA'S working on another puzzle! Can you help her by drawing the correct symbol to finish each sequence?

TOTALLY *True* OR FREAKISHLY FALSE

Howl much do you know about the student bodies of Monster High? Awaken your brain and decide if these statements are true or false. Tick your answers, then check them on page 175!

1. Skelita Calaveras hails from Scaris, the City of Frights.

TRUE ⬭ FALSE ⬭

2. Howleen is Clawdeen Wolf's little sister.

TRUE ⬭ FALSE ⬭

3. Cleo de Nile's monster pet is a snake called Hissette.

TRUE ⬭ FALSE ⬭

4. Catty Noir is a famous casketball star.

TRUE ⬭ FALSE ⬭

5. Twyla is the daughter of the Boogey Man.

TRUE ◯ FALSE ◯

6. Purrsephone and Toralei are twin sisters.

TRUE ◯ FALSE ◯

7. Gigi Grant loves being stuck in small spaces.

TRUE ◯ FALSE ◯

8. If you want your portrait sketched, you should ask Catrine de Mew.

TRUE ◯ FALSE ◯

9. Ghoulia Yelps cannot function without a schedule.

TRUE ◯ FALSE ◯

10. Draculaura only has fangs for Deuce Gorgon.

TRUE ◯ FALSE ◯

Scare-itage

Mr Hackington™ has asked the student bodies to give presentations about the most important things they own. For Cleo, it's her wedges ... duh! But Skelita's prize possession is a boo-tiful necklace handed down to her by her grandmother. Ugh-mazingly, it's been in her *familia* for 10 generations! After the presentation, Skelita's necklace mysteriously ends up in the Monster High catacombs. Can you help her retrieve the Calaveras heirloom?

START

FINISH

ANSWERS ON PAGE 175

Drop-dead Gore-geous

Here's a blank canvas, courtesy of Catty Noir, for you to design a fierce new outfit for your favourite ghoul. Will you go for geek chic or goth chic? Fierce fashionista or scary-cute? Does your ghoul play it safe in comfy baggies or is she a tween trendsetter? You decide!

107

HORRO-MANCE FOR HOWLEEN

It's the first full moon of the lunar leap year and horro-mance is in the air. Clawdeen warns her little sister, Howleen, to be scareful. But why? Find out by cracking the creeperific code below.

H O W L E E N

H A S A

C R U S H O N

R O M U L U S

ZOMBIE-DOKU

Ghoulia I-urgh-ves testing her intelligence. Help her by completing this zombie-doku she's working on. Each of the numbers, 1 to 6, should appear once in each column, row and box.

	5			1	
6			2	5	4
		2			5
		6			1
	2		5		
3				4	

SLUMBER PARTY:
YETI-STYLE!

The ghouls are having a slumber party at **ABBEY'S** house. It's so cold that they need their slippers.

Find the slipper stickers and stick them on the feet of the correct ghoul.

THE Ghoulest SEASON

Mr Rotter™ has set his class a new assignment. They must create a vision board showing what they think is the ghoulest season. Distracted by Frankie's ugh-mazing collection of Teen Scream, the ghouls are focusing more on fashion than weather.... Can you figure out who said what about each season? Write their names in the white boxes, using the pictures on the opposite page as clues. Which season wins the most votes overall?

1 Personally, I like autumn. It's not quite summer and it's not quite winter – it doesn't really know what it is. I know a lot of ghouls who feel a bit like that! Plus I like all the different colours, and the fact you can start wearing more layers. I like to keep my seams warm because then there's less chance of my limbs falling apart!

2 What could be better than spring? It's the season when everything blossoms and grows. I am a total sucker for baby animals and anything with the teensiest bit of scary-cuteness! Oh, and spring is also great because you can get out your sun umbrella.

3 Everyone loves summer, surely? I guess coming from the Great Barrier Reef kind of affects my decision but I just can't get enough of seawater and the beach – and kicking back in my baggies and flip-flops! Also, everyone tends to be more chilled out in the summer and I like that.

4 Winter is the best. The colder air makes it easier for your brain to absorb vital knowledge. Summer heat leaves you feeling less motivated to do ghoulwork – unless you're me, of course! Besides which, when it's cold you can always put more clothes on. But when it's hot, it's not so easy to cool down.

5 I'm not bothered about any one season in particular. Interesting hauntings and happenings go on all year round at Monster High! Just let me know what the final outcome of this debate is. If the results are interesting enough, I might publish them in The Ghost Post.

6 Oh. My. Ra! Do you even have to ask? With my royal Egyptian roots, I adore the summer heat. I have to be careful about protecting my flawless skin from the sun, of course, but my bandages do most of the work. Eww, wrinkles – unthinkable!

Autumn is just swell! It sets off my hotrod-red victory-roll hairdo and is filled with just the sweetest songs of change. Autumn is most definitely the best season, doll!

Winter is time to be quiet and reflective. Recommend to wear fur and lot of layers. Without winter, is no snow and no snow, NO SNOW BOOTS. Winter is ghoulest season - is fact! Can go sledging, climb glacier, build snowman.

Fashion-wise, I don't have a favourite season because I can find fierce looks all year round. But in terms of my other love, sport, it has to be summer. It's the season with the most track-and-field events and, although they won't let me compete in my platforms, nothing beats that feeling of competing ... it's the beast!

SEASON	NUMBER OF VOTES
SPRING	
SUMMER	
AUTUMN	
WINTER	
NO FAVOURITE	

ANSWERS ON PAGE 175

The winning season is

_____

113

Clawdeen, Abbey and Spectra all love to experiment with eye-shadow colours. Grab your colouring pencils (a.k.a. eyeliner and make-up brushes) and try out some creeperific colours on their eyelids. How about some frosty pinks and icy blues? Next, move on to their cheeks and lips. Will they be bold and daring or perfectly pale?

GUY STYLE

Let's face it, the ghouls at Monster High are pretty chic. But let's not fur-get about the guys!
Try this biteable boy-based quiz to find out how much you squeally know about their styles.
The answers are in the panel below and one of the names can be used twice.

1. Which school hottie rocks a snake-hawk? _____

2. Which werewolf is super self-conscious about his shedding problem? _____

3. Which normie student loves a buttoned shirt and bowtie combo? _____

4. Which son of a river monster is unable to wear anything with a tight collar? _____

5. Who wears a jacket with sleeves reflecting his favourite colours, red and yellow? _____

6. Which zombie student considers fashion decisions a waste of valuable brain power? _____

7. Which casual student refers to his style as 'blipster'? _____

8. Which sensitive student shows an appreciation for anything carefully stitched? _____

9. Which hot-headed student-DJ truly believes his style is on fire? _____

10. Which guy is considered to be one half of Monster High's stylish 'It' couple? _____

Clawd Wolf • Holt Hyde™ • HooDude Voodoo • Gil Webber™ • Slo Mo
Heath Burns™ • Invisi Billy • Deuce Gorgon • Jackson Jekyll

ANSWERS ON PAGE 175

JOBS FOR THE GHOULS

Draculaura has convinced Abbey to host a makeover slumber party in her ice cave. ['s] super chilled until the ghouls start arguing over who's in charge of each makeover [st]ation! Can you guess who made each statement? Fill in their name below, then choose [t]he job that would be beast for them. Use the ghouls' names and jobs listed below.

A I'm sure you'll all agree that I'd be the beast fashion stylist. What's that, Cleo? You'd give me a run for my money? Are you sure about that? Fancy a trip to the race track?

B I don't really mind what I do. I am pretty good at make-up – I've managed to perfect my own, even without being able to see my reflection!

C I do beauty. Am knowing good tricks for warming face in ice cave. Is decided.

D Uuuugh ooooo arrrrrrgh! (Translation: I can work the camera.)

E Just look at my divine cuticles! I keep a lot of freaktacular nail secrets under wraps so if you ghouls are lucky, I might divulge one or two…. Then again, I might not.

F Crikey, ghouls! I'm not much good behind a camera and I'm only a pro when it comes to waterproof make-up. How about I do a spot of modelling for you?

G As I've mastered the electrified look, I have no problems working with fried or frazzled hair. I'll soon put some unlife back into any lack-lustre locks!

A
Ghoul: _____
Job: _____

B
Ghoul: _____
Job: _____

C
Ghoul: _____
Job: _____

D
Ghoul: _____
Job: _____

E
Ghoul: _____
Job: _____

F
Ghoul: _____
Job: _____

G
Ghoul: _____
Job: _____

JOBS
Model
Beautician
Fashion stylist
Nail technician
Hairstylist
Photographer
Make-up artist

GHOULS
Frankie Stein
Abbey Bominable
Draculaura
Cleo de Nile
Clawdeen Wolf
Ghoulia Yelps
Lagoona Blue

ANSWERS ON PAGE 175

MONSTER PETS

Here are more Monster High student bodies with their beast friends. Find the stickers that match the monster pet silhouettes!

RHUEN

My phantom furittus (that's 'ferret' to you!).

CAPTAIN PENNY

Every penguin needs a rocket pack to fly.

SHIVER

A woolly mammoth with a tough hide.

118

ROUX

Griffins make the best beasties!

CHEWLIAN

He's got a snappy personality.

PERSEUS

Two tails and loads of rat-i-chewed!

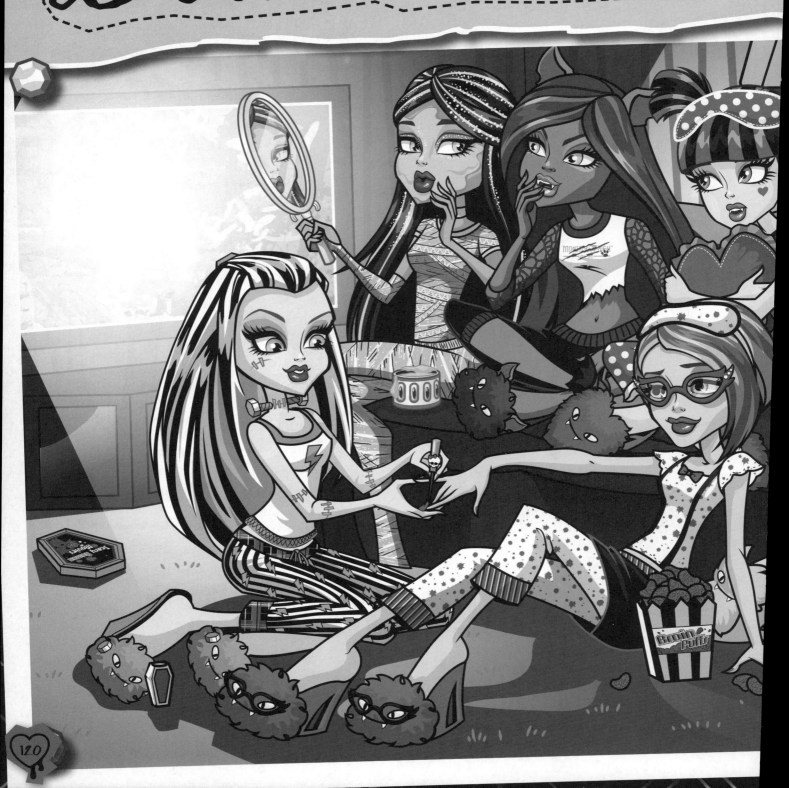

After a scare-raising day at the Maul, these beasties can't resist
a vampering session. From fur-rocious slippers to fangtastic face masks,
they have everything they need for some totally ghoulish fang-out time.
Give yourself one minute to slurp in this sleepover shot, then cover
up the picture and see how many questions you can answer!

1. How many ghouls are in the picture?

_____

2. What shape is Frankie's nail-varnish bottle?

_____

3. Which ghoul is on the far right of the picture?

_____

4. How many ghouls have eye masks on their heads?

_____

5. Which student has her hair in bunches?

_____

6. Who is sitting between Draculaura and Cleo?

_____

7. What does Frankie have on her vest top?

_____

8. Whose slippers are wearing glasses?

_____

9. What is Cleo holding?

_____

ANSWERS ON PAGE 175

YOUR StUDeNt Profile

You know all about the student bodies at Monster High, but they want to know all about you! Create your own student profile on this page.

NAME:

AGE:

FREAKY FLAW:

FAVOURITE FOOD:

FAVOURITE COLOUR:

FAVOURITE ACTIVITY:

KILLER STYLE:

PET:

PET PEEVE:

CREATE a Monster

If you could put together a scary-cool new Monster High student, who would they be and what would they look like? Let your imagination run wild and sketch their hair, make-up and killer style.

123

UGHSOME *Accessories*

Cleo and Clawdeen don't agree on much, but they do agree on their favourite colour: gold. They rarely go anywhere without their bling! These ghouls all want to look a bit more 'golden', but they're feeling a bit clueless.... Can you help them?

Draw some fierce new glasses on Ghoulia and some chunky bracelets on Lagoona. Rochelle would like a new handbag on her arm while Robecca doesn't know what she wants! Accessorize these ghouls with some so-this-century bling, add some inspired new patterns on their clothes, then get them glowing with some ugh-mazing colours.

SCAREDROBE Essentials

Slo Mo

Frankie Stein

Ghoulia Yelps

Heath Burns

Elissabat

Mr Hackington

A. I wouldn't be me without my bolts. They're electrifying!

B. IT'S GOTTA BE MY SIGNATURE SHADES. WITHOUT THEM, EVERYONE WOULD BE ROCKIN' THE SAME STONE-COLD STYLE, IF YOU GET ME!

C. My horn-rimmed glasses, of course! I couldn't see, or be me, without them.

D. My lacy umbrella so I can take the occasional walk in the sun.

E. Is obvious, no? My fur!

F. My essential item would be anything with ruffles.

Every ghoul or guy has at least one item they can't unlive without. Using your eek-stensive knowledge of Monster High fashions, can you match each character with the right style statement? Draw a lightning bolt to connect each perfect pair.

G. My beanie. I totally unlive in it, along with my hoodie and cut-off jeans.

H. I ALWAYS WEAR THE SAME THINGS: JEANS AND A T-SHIRT, SNEAKERS AND MY MONSTER LETTER JACKET. I GUESS THE JACKET IS MY FAVOURITE.

I. My helmet: I can't breathe without it!

J. MY FLAME-SLEEVED JACKET: THE GHOULS GO MAD FOR IT!

K. My cape and riding boots. Oh, and my head, of course!

L. My apron. It protects my mad tie in lessons.

Headmistress Bloodgood

Draculaura

Gil Webber

Deuce Gorgon

Invisi Billy

Abbey Bominable

ANSWERS ON PAGE 175

127

Sleep is a vital part of any ghoul's beauty regime and these ghouls know it. After counting bats to drift off, they're now enjoying a quiet nightmare or four. But despite the ghouls practising the same bedtime routine every night, one picture in each row below is not quite the same as the others. Can you spot the odd ones out?

ANSWERS ON PAGE 175

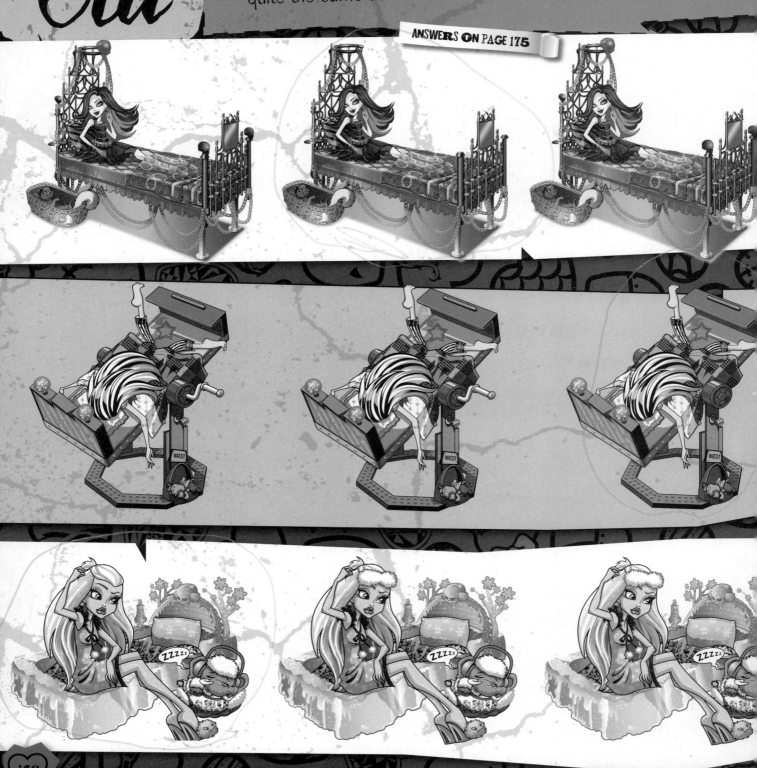

Nail It!

Cleo rocks up late to the charity fundraiser bake-off. Why? Because she's just had her nails done! The polish is made from ink extract of the giant mutant octopus – not the kind of thing you want to chip while handling cookie dough.... Can you unscramble these words before the mutant cookie monster devours everything? They're all names of nail polishes in Cleo's beauty cabinet. The initial letters have been filled in to give you a headless start. If you get stuck, check out the panel of answers below!

1. TRENDICISE SCAREM
2. STYFOR EWITH
3. PERCEY SCORNIM
4. SCATISKTULL TRACELS
5. SHALLOWMARM MENSORT
6. FOFEET LEPAP
7. SHERE MIGHTRANE
8. QUIETAN EGRY
9. SCATTIFANG
10. MEDALS IN SITDRESS
11. PIPOLOLL
12. NOSET CLOD
13. LICETREC BUEL

1. I _ _ _ _ _ _ _ _ _ S _ _ _ _ _
2. F _ _ _ _ _ W _ _ _ _
3. C _ _ _ _ _ C _ _ _ _ _ _
4. S _ _ _ _ _ _ _ _ _ S _ _ _ _ _
5. M _ _ _ _ _ _ _ _ _ _ M _ _ _ _ _ _
6. T _ _ _ _ _ A _ _ _ _
7. S _ _ _ N _ _ _ _ _ _ _
8. A _ _ _ _ _ _ G _ _ _
9. F _ _ _ _ _ _ _ _ _
10. D _ _ _ _ IN D _ _ _ _ _ _ _
11. L _ _ _ _ _ _ _
12. S _ _ _ _ C _ _ _
13. E _ _ _ _ _ _ B _ _ _

ANSWERS ON PAGE 175

MARSHMALLOW MONSTER • CREEPY CRIMSON
SKULLTASTIC SCARLET • TOFFEE APPLE • LOLLIPOP
DAMSEL IN DISTRESS • FROSTY WHITE • ELECTRIC BLUE
STONE COLD • FANGTASTIC • ANTIQUE GREY
IRIDESCENT SCREAM • SHEER NIGHTMARE

129

Grim Grid

Feast your eyes, ghouls! This grim grid (a.k.a. creeptastic crossword) is a real monster! Fill in the freaky facts, then use the letters in the grey boxes to spell the name of a ghoul who loves to mix rot iron and stained glass with her scaredrobe choices!

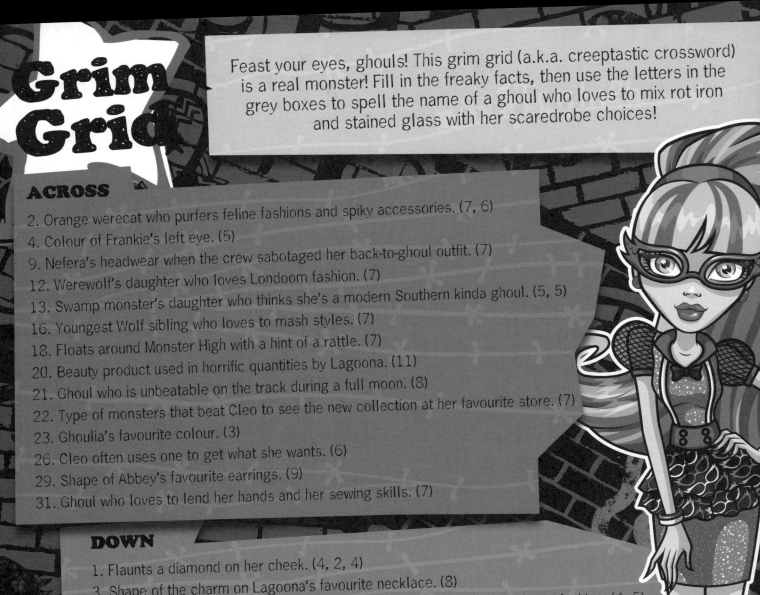

ACROSS

2. Orange werecat who purfers feline fashions and spiky accessories. (7, 6)
4. Colour of Frankie's left eye. (5)
9. Nefera's headwear when the crew sabotaged her back-to-ghoul outfit. (7)
12. Werewolf's daughter who loves Londoom fashion. (7)
13. Swamp monster's daughter who thinks she's a modern Southern kinda ghoul. (5, 5)
16. Youngest Wolf sibling who loves to mash styles. (7)
18. Floats around Monster High with a hint of a rattle. (7)
20. Beauty product used in horrific quantities by Lagoona. (11)
21. Ghoul who is unbeatable on the track during a full moon. (8)
22. Type of monsters that beat Cleo to see the new collection at her favourite store. (7)
23. Ghoulia's favourite colour. (3)
26. Cleo often uses one to get what she wants. (6)
29. Shape of Abbey's favourite earrings. (9)
31. Ghoul who loves to lend her hands and her sewing skills. (7)

DOWN

1. Flaunts a diamond on her cheek. (4, 2, 4)
3. Shape of the charm on Lagoona's favourite necklace. (8)
5. Genie's daughter who chooses comfort and natural fabrics over high-end fashion. (4, 5)
6. Cleo's most prized possession. (6)
7. Zen ghoul who loves to fire up traditional clothes with Chinese accessories. (8, 4)
8. Worn around Venus McFlytrap's wrists. (5)
10. Student known as 'makeover ghoul'. (8)
11. Mutant creature that contributes to Cleo's Iridescent Scream nail varnish. (7)
13. Shape of Draculaura's beauty mark. (5)
14. These form part of Viperine's mane of ssscary-cool hair. (6)
15. Often wears safety pin earrings. (10)
17. Colour of Robecca Steam's eyes. (6)
18. Mind-reading ghoul who rocks a green '60s vibe. (6, 7)
19. Dude who loves the patchwork look. (7)
24. Singer who loves flashy, larger-than-unlife outfits. (5, 4)
25. One half of a pair of twins who like to match fashions. (11)
27. Nefera's favourite shade of lipstick. (4, 4)
28. Last name of ghoul who seeks out faux fur and jungle prints. (9)
30. Piece of jewellery worn by Holt Hyde. (7, 4)

The ghoul who loves to mix rot iron and stained glass is _ _ _ _ _ _ _ _ _ _ _ _ _ _

ANSWERS ON PAGE 175

Fashion FAIL!

Howleen is always reinventing herself, wanting to stand out from the pack. She loves to mash together different styles, but not all of her fashion experiments are successful. Clawdeen says her little sister often looks like she got dressed in the dark! Can you help Howleen transform her outfit from voltageous fail to howlin' hot with this word ladder? Complete the clues to help you, changing only one letter at a time. Use the answer panel below if you get freaked out!

TALL   BAWL   TAIL
BOWL   HALL   BALL

FAIL

_ _ _ _   Jinafire Long has one of these.

_ _ _ _   How Draculaura might look if she borrowed Clawdeen's wedges.

_ _ _ _   Rochelle wanted to be a monitor of this.

_ _ _ _   Deuce needs one of these for a casket-related game.

_ _ _ _   Cleo might do this if she broke a nail!

_ _ _ _   Blood soup is served in one of these in the Creepateria.

HOWL

ANSWERS ON PAGE 176

132

JUNGLE BOO-GIE

The Monster High Jungle Dance is coming up. The student body has nominated one ghoul to be Jungle Queen, but this ghoul has only just started fanging out with the others and is still a bit shy. The nomination has left her head in a spin. Use this word spiral to find the name of the reluctant Jungle Queen, circling every third letter and writing those letters on the lines below.

START HERE

H Q J I O A K E N M M E L A B Q I O V X O G H L F P I V M W T U C T B G L K P E

The Jungle Queen is _ _ _ _ _ _ _ _ _ _ _ _ _ _

ANSWERS ON PAGE 176

133

UPLOADING PIC.....

It's the Homecarnage Dance and **SPECTRA** has uploaded a pic to her blog. But someone messed with the picture before it was published!

HERE'S THE ORIGINAL PHOTO ...

... AND HERE'S
WHAT WAS POSTED!

Can you spot 10 things that have
been changed? Add a sticker
below for each difference
you spot.

What's that, WATZIT?

Frankie's scary-cute puppy, Watzit, is made of spare parts. He was created by her dad, Frankenstein. What an ugh-mazing present! If you could create your own pet, what parts of what animals would you use? List them below, and then draw your mash-up monster pet!

We're both stitched together with style!

Pet Profile

Name: Watzit™
Owner: Frankie Stein™
Type of creature: Puppy made from spare parts
Scary-cool fact: Built by Frankie's dad as a present for her.

My mash-up pet:

The head of ....

The tail of ....

The legs of ....

The body of ....

Name ....

In the shadows

Draculaura carries a frilly umbrella so that she can take an occasional walk in the sun. Her pet, Count Fabulous, prefers the dark and lives in the shadows, but his style is totally matched

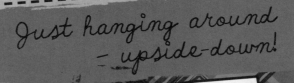

Just hanging around — upside-down!

Pet Profile

Name: Count Fabulous™
Owner: Draculaura™
Type of creature: Bat
Scary-cool fact: He's Draculaura's BFF (Bat Friend Forever).

A bat with my scary-cool style:

Odd KITTEN Out

When there's a full moon, Clawdeen can see in the dark – just like her cat, Crescent, can! Use your super-sight to spot and then circle the odd kitten out in each row.

We're both purr-fect.

Pet Profile

Name: Crescent™
Owner: Clawdeen Wolf™
Type of creature: Kitten
Scary-cool fact: This scary-cute little kitten is as fuzzy as her owner.

ANSWERS ON
PAGE 176

Robots + rain = rust

Both Robecca and her mechanical penguin, Captain Penny, are rocket-powered robots! No robot likes rain, so lead them both through the maze to meet in the middle where there's some shelter from a spooktacular storm. Watch out for the lightning!

Let's go! Full scream ahead.

Pet Profile

Name: Captain Penny™
Owner: Robecca Steam™
Type of creature:
Mechanical penguin
Scary-cool fact: Comes equipped with her own personal rocket pack.

FINISH

FINISH

START

ANSWERS ON PAGE 176

CHEWLIAN'S new look

Venus puts on eco-inspired fashion shows and believes in recycling. So when her pet Venus flytrap, Chewlian, wants a new plant pot, she decides to give his old one a plant-tastic makeover instead! Style Chewlian's pot to match each of Venus's ugh-mazing outfits.

Be bright, be bold, be involved!

Pet Profile

Name: Chewlian™
Owner: Venus McFlytrap™
Type of creature: Venus flytrap
Scary-cool fact: He's got a really snappy personality!

Shiver's SEQUENCES

Abbey can freeze some objects with her touch and ghouls with her words, but she does have a warm heart! Shiver, a woolly mammoth, is her not-so-sensitive pet. Complete each sequence by working out which pose of Shiver goes in the space.

If truth hurts, put ice on it.

Pet Profile

Name: Shiver™
Owner: Abbey Bominable™
Type of creature: Woolly mammoth
Scary-cool fact: It would be very hard to hurt her feelings. Which is just as well, being Abbey's pet!

ANSWERS ON PAGE 176

A complete puzzle!

Ghoulia is great at solving problems and puzzles for her GFFs. Can you solve this puzzle by adding the missing letters to the spaces to make five words that rhyme with 'owl'? Use your brain and remember to think outside of the coffin, just like Ghoulia!

You can't hurry genius.

Pet Profile

Name: Sir Hoots A Lot™
Owner: Ghoulia Yelps™
Type of creature: Owl
Scary-cool fact: An intelligent companion for brainbox Ghoulia, but he refuses to carry messages for her.

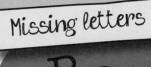
Missing letters

S P C R H G F R

1. _ _ owl
2. _ owl
3. _ _ owl
4. _ owl
5. _ _ owl

ANSWERS ON PAGE 176

A FREAKILY unique FRIEND

Are you feeling creepily creative like Catrine DeMew? Then let your imagination run wild, show off your artistic abilities and create your very own clawsome creature here! Will it have fangs, claws or horns? Will it be furry, scaly or feathery? Well, whatever it will be, it's sure to be freakily unique, just like its owner!

Pet Profile

Name:

Owner:

Type of creature:

Scary-cool fact:

145

PIXELATED PETS

Spectra, Operetta and Twyla have each found their perfect animal companion. But their pictures are missing! Figure out who is who on the next page and write their names in the boxes. Now draw the pets in the circles below.

Pet Profile

Name: Rhuen™
Owner: Spectra Vondergeist™
Type of creature: Ghost ferret
Scary-cool fact: The name ferret comes from the Latin 'furittus', which means 'little thief'.

Pet Profile

Name: Memphis 'Daddy O' Longlegs™
Owner: Operetta™
Type of creature: Spider
Scary-cool fact: He's not like any other spider you've ever seen....

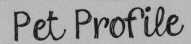

Pet Profile

Name: Dustin™
Owner: Twyla™
Type of creature: Dust bunny
Scary-cool fact: Twyla adopted Dustin after she found him blowing in the wind.

Pet:

Pet:

Pet:

a

b

c

ANSWERS ON PAGE 176

A STICKY SITUATION

Wydowna's got her web all in a tangle today! Can you lead her little pet housefly, Shoo, through the giant maze, without getting stuck in any sticky cobwebs?

I love lending a helping hand. Lots of them.

Pet Profile

Name: Shoo™
Owner: Wydowna Spider™
Type of creature: Housefly
Scary-cool fact: She supplies
Wydowna with many
a buzzworthy moment!

START

FINISH

ANSWERS ON PAGE 176

AQUATIC arm candy

The ghouls of Monster High think that handbags look dead stylish and they have a different one to suit each outfit. But Lagoona has a very special bag ... it's actually a fishbowl so she can secretly take her pet piranha, Neptuna, to class!

Monster waves, killer style!

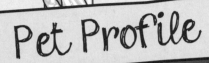

Pet Profile

Name: Neptuna™
Owner: Lagoona Blue™
Type of creature: Piranha
Scary-cool fact: Enjoys nipping other monsters when they least expect it.

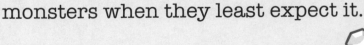

Draw your own freaky fish friend in this fishbowl purse.

TRUE OR FALSE

Are you Monster High's biggest fan?
Test your knowledge with this creeperific quiz!
Stick a 'true' or 'false' sticker next to each
statement, then check your answers.

1 Frankie sometimes falls apart – literally. FALSE

2 Cleo's sister is called Nefertiti. TRUE

3 Operetta is Rochelle Goyle's pet. FALSE

4 The lockers at Monster High are coffin-shaped. TRUE

5 Cleo is the captain of the Fear Squad. TRUE

6 Draculaura can turn into a bat whenever she wants to. TRUE

7 Deuce can turn people to stone. TRUE

8 Toralei Stripe is best friends with Clawdeen. FALSE

9 Sloman 'Slo Mo' Mortavitch is a zombie. FALSE

10 Bloodgood is Monster High's headless headmistress.

ANSWERS ON PAGE 176

HANDBAG MIX-UP

The ghouls' handbags are all mixed up!
Draw lines to match each ghoul with
her own bag (the one that matches
her unique scary-cool style).

Snakes ALIVE!

Viperine is never without her pets – in fact, they're always in her hair! With her nest of rather active vipers, Viperine really doesn't have room in her unlife for any other pet. Can you draw lines to link each close-up with the correct viper?

Some people wave, some high five, some hug.... I bite.

ANSWERS ON PAGE 176

MONSTROUS MIX-UP

There's been a mix-up of the most monstrous kind! Can you rearrange the letters to spell out some of the scary-cute creatures found at Monster High?

1. camechalin genupin

_ _ _ _ _ _ _ _ _ _   _ _ _ _ _ _ _

2. evnsu flapytr

_ _ _ _ _   _ _ _ _ _ _

3. ggoyarle ffgriin

_ _ _ _ _ _ _ _   _ _ _ _ _ _ _

4. owolyl mothmam

_ _ _ _ _ _   _ _ _ _ _ _

5. stgho refter

_ _ _ _ _   _ _ _ _ _

6. tsud nbuyn

_ _ _ _   _ _ _ _ _

7. garylego dogllbu

_ _ _ _ _ _ _   _ _ _ _ _ _ _

8. rabsca btleee

_ _ _ _ _ _   _ _ _ _ _

Colourful CREATURES

Rockseena and Roux, two totally rockin' gargoyle pets at Monster High, are feeling a little grey today. You can cheer them up by giving them a colourful restyle here! Will you echo the style of their owners, Clawd and Rochelle, or experiment with a completely new look?

Pet Profile

Name: Rockseena™
Owner: Clawd Wolf™
Type of creature: Gargoyle Bulldog
Scary-cool fact: She is Clawd's number-one, rock-solid fan.

Pet Profile

Name: Roux™
Owner: Rochelle Goyle™
Type of creature: Gargoyle
griffin
Scary-cool fact: She has
been Rochelle's pet from
 the time she hatched.

Bell-Tower Beauties

Rochelle and I can both be found floating around the bell tower. I monster-watch from up here, looking for inspiration for my column. Rochelle just feels most at home when she's near (or on) the roof.

How well do you know Monster High's bell-tower beauties? Underline the words that sum up Rochelle in grey and those that make you think of Spectra in purple.

Rock Candy   Violet   Protective

Griffin   Silk   Angel Cake   Pale

Rhuen   Persistent   Transparent

Floating   Disgruntled   Chains

Roux   Scaris   Kind   Haunting

Defensive   Ferret   Curious

Iron   Stained Glass   Journalism

Architecture   Pigeons   Sculpting

Rattle   Ghostly Gossip   Grey

Spectra and Rochelle have a ghoul's-eye view of comings and groanings at Monster High. What do you think they've just spotted? Draw the scene here!

Ssssnake STYLE

Golden ghoul Cleo has the most regal pet at Monster High – an Egyptian royal cobra. Just like her owner, Hissette knows how to axe-cessorize and always wears fangtastic gold jewellery. Use the space below to design some sssscary-cool new jewellery for her.

You can't keep royalty under wraps.

Pet Profile

Name: Hissette™
Owner: Cleo de Nile™
Type of creature: Egyptian cobra
Scary-cool fact: Her hiss is much worse than her, er, somewhat poisonous bite.

Collect 'em, count 'em

Toralei has a scary-cute sabre-toothed tiger cub called Sweet Fangs. She's the purr-fect pet for Toralei, as they both have orange fur, dark stripes and green eyes. Count up the bones that Sweet Fangs has collected today and add the total to the box.

You can't teach an old cat new tricks.

Pet Profile

Name: Sweet Fangs™
Owner: Toralei Stripe™
Type of creature: Sabre-toothed tiger cub
Scary-cool fact: She's much cuddlier than her owner!

Sweet Fangs collected ⬤ bones today.

ANSWERS ON PAGE 176

ANSWERS ON PAGE 176

GHOUL RULES

ROCHELLE is the head of the safety team at Monster High and she knows that two of these school rules are wrong. Do you know which ones? Put a cross next to them. Now check your answers. If you were right, give yourself a gold Safety Badge sticker!

1
All monsters must eat meat at lunchtimes in the creepateria.

2
No heads, hands or feet should be separated from bodies during school hours.

3
Students should venture only into the known areas of the catacombs – no further!

4
All zombies should start heading to class half an hour early. Slowness is no excuse for lateness!

5
Always look Deuce Gorgon in the eyes when his sunglasses are off.

DESIGN a LOGO

After their success at Monster Mashionals, the **FEAR SQUAD** is getting a new look. Design them a logo and add it to their flag. Go ghouls, go!

The REAL beetle

Nefera often returns to Monster High, bringing her pet beetle, Azura, with her. Can you work out which beetle below is the real Azura? Seven of them have freaky flaws that Nefera would never put up with!

I rule alone.

Pet Profile

Name: Azura™
Owner: Nefera de Nile™
Type of creature: Scarab beetle
Scary-cool fact: The name Azura comes from the word 'azure', which is a shade of blue that is similar to his colour.

ANSWERS ON PAGE 176

CUSTOMIZE Cushion

Howleen looks ugh-mazing at the moment with her hot pink hair! And so does her hedgehog, Cushion, with her bright pink spikes. Howleen is always changing her style in order to stand out from the pack and her pet is no different. But what other shades would suit Cushion's spikes? Conduct a colourful experiment here!

I want to howl at my own moon.

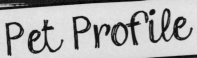

Pet Profile

Name: Cushion™
Owner: Howleen Wolf™
Type of creature: Hedgehog
Scary-cool fact: She's prickly on the outside, but actually really sweet on the inside.

Say WHAT?

Headmistress Bloodgood has an important message for the pupils of Monster High, but she's been swamped with paperwork and hasn't had time to spell it out for them. Can you crack the cryptic code to work out what it says?

W A T C H   O U T   F O R

P I R A N H A S   I N

T H E   P O O L !

 W
 U
 R
 N
 E

 T
 F
 P
 S
 L

 O
 A
 I
 C
 H

CLAWSOME WORDSEARCH

There are many fur-bulous animals found at Monster High. Can you find the grr-oup of eight listed below in the big grid? If you can, you'll really have something to howl about!

```
L  I  K  N  E  T  T  I  K  P
V  R  H  O  F  F  G  K  P  I
S  H  X  E  R  J  N  K  Z  R
C  V  M  L  D  E  Z  L  Y  A
V  E  M  E  J  G  D  F  H  N
T  S  A  M  G  K  E  I  V  H
A  P  L  A  E  Z  F  H  P  A
B  W  H  H  Q  E  F  V  O  S
O  U  M  C  D  Q  V  N  C  G
H  O  U  S  E  F  L  Y  E  M
```

Bat
Kitten
Owl
Spider

Housefly
Piranha
Hedgehog
Chameleon

ANSWERS ON PAGE 176

167

ANSWERS ON PAGE 176

Date Dilemma

Abbey hasn't yet found a date for the Dance of the Dead. Now she's starting to freak out! Her GFFs have set up a speed-dating (or 'hurry-up-dating' as Abbey calls it) event to help her bag a monster for the evening. Read what each one has to say for himself, then draw lines to match the notes to the names at the bottom of the page.

A

WELL HELLO GHOULFRIEND, YOU'RE LOOKING PRETTY HOT FOR ONE SO COLD! HOW'D YOU LIKE ME TO TAKE YOU TO THE DANCE OF THE DEAD? YOU'D BE HEAD AND SHOULDERS ABOVE THE DANCE FLOOR CROWD SO AT LEAST I'D GET TO SEE YOU FROM MY DJ BOOTH. I'VE BEEN SINGLE SINCE SPLITTING FROM HOTTIE FRANKIE STEIN. STICK WITH ME AND WE'LL SET THE SCHOOL ON FIRE!

B

I just came along with a friend, to see what's what really, I've got casketball practice in a minute, so I gotta go and anyway, I'm kinda dating this cute pink-wearing vampire.

C

A DATE? THIS IS WHAT YOU'RE DOING SITTING HERE? I WONDERED WHY THERE WAS AN EMPTY TABLE AND A HUGE LINE OF MONSTERS. LISTEN, YOU'RE KINDA COOL AND EVERYTHING, BUT MY GHOULFRIEND WOULD UNLEASH A THOUSAND EVIL CURSES ON ME IF I EVER CHEATED ON HER.

D

Wow, oh, I can't believe I'm here, at this event, with you and, like, this isn't normally the kind of thing I get to do, but ever since Frankie brought me to life as her fake boyfriend I've been looking for a creeperific ghoul to hang out with, can you pick me, plieeeease?

E

HEY, GHOUL, YOU'RE LOOKING SCARY-COOL. WANT SOME HOT STUFF TO WARM THE PLACE WHERE YOUR ICY HEART SHOULD BE? IF SO, CALL OFF YOUR SEARCH. I AM THE HOTTEST MONSTER AT MONSTER HIGH. I'M ALSO THE FASTEST. WHAT? CLAWDEEN BEAT ME? THAT'S JUST A RUMOUR! ANYWAY, DON'T BE AN ICE QUEEN, LET THE MOST UGHSOME MONSTER IN SCHOOL THAW YOU OUT!

F

UGHGHHH, EERRRRR, YUGGGG, UGGGGGGG, EEEEEEERGH, GHOULia, UGHHHHH, aRRGHHHH, EEEEEERM.

CLAWD WOLF

HOODUDE VOODOO

DEUCE GORGON

HOLT HYDE

HEATH BURNS

SLO MO

The Monster Wish List

Hey ghoulfriend! Don't know about you, but we can't wait to find out what spooktastic shocks and creeperific surprises the next year has in store for Monster High! Think about the next year of your monster life and use this page to write down all your hopes and wishes — from learning a scary-cool skill to throwing an ughsome party. Here's hoping all your screams come true!

It's a HOOT!

Ghoulia has some genius, scary-funny jokes to make your ghoulfriends giggle – translated from zombie, of corpse! Sir Hoots A Lot thinks they're hilarious!

Q. How do monsters like their eggs?
A. Terror fried.

Q. What's a vampire's favourite sport?
A. Batminton.

Q. What do you do with a green monster?
A. Leave it in the sun until it ripens!

Q. Why do werewolves do well at school?
A. Because when they're asked a question, they come up with a snappy answer.

Q. How does a yeti get to work?
A. By icicle.

Q. What do vampires have at 11 o'clock every day?
A. A coffin break.

Q. On which day do monsters like to eat out?
A. Chewsday.

Q. Why was Baron Frankenstein never lonely?
A. Because he was good at making friends.

Q. What do you call a dog owned by Dracula?
A. A bloodhound.

Q. Where do Abominable Snowmen go to dance?
A. To snowballs.

Now write your beast monster joke here!

Q.

....

....

A.

....

....

ANSWERS ON PAGE 176

PSYCHIC Scarah

Scarah Screams has a terror-ific talent – she can hear other monsters' thoughts! Test your own psychic power by matching these wicked wonderings to the monster who's thinking them.

1

2

3

4

5

A Oh my Ra! If I don't get the lead part in the school play, I'm going to unravel!

B I am not understanding this way of falling head over the heels for boys.

C Why can't every monster at school just put their empty cans in the recycling bin?

D MAN, CLEO IS AWESOME, BUT TONIGHT I REALLY WANT TO HANG OUT WITH MY BROS.

E DON'T SET THIS BOOK ON FIRE, DON'T SET THIS BOOK ON FIRE...

172

THIS IS MY MONSTER high!

Imagine you're a student at Monster High! Who would be in your skeleton crew? Fill in your freaky-fab facts below.

MY SKELETON CREW WOULD INCLUDE:

I'D BE CRUSHING ON:
(add a sticker of your monster crush)

MY FAVOURITE ACTIVITY WOULD BE:

MY MONSTER STYLE WOULD BE:
(draw a picture of yourself)

MY BEAST FRIEND WOULD BE:
(add a sticker of your fave ghoul)

THE CLASSES I WOULD LIKE BEST WOULD BE:

PAGES 82-83

... be an A-list star of stage and scream.

... help out a ghoulfriend in need.

... fly off into the sunset with the monster of her nightmares.

... design a fur-rocious pair of killer heels.

... go on a fangtastic trip around the world.

... be the next spookily smart headmistress of Monster High.

... become a Scultimate Roller Maze commentator.

PAGES 84-85

1. Draculaura – D, **2.** HooDude Voodoo – A,
3. Frankie Stein – B, **4.** Clawdeen Wolf – C
5. Operetta – F, **6.** Cleo de Nile – E

PAGE 86

1. Venus, **2.** Draculaura, **3.** Cleo, **4.** Frankie,
5. Ghoulia, **6.** Abbey, **7.** Catty, **8.** Clawdeen

PAGES 88-89

Catty Noir – MAGENTA
Slo Mo – PURPLE
Jinafire Long – ROYAL RED
Lagoona Blue – OCEAN BLUE
Deuce Gorgon – NEON GREEN
Scarah Screams – GREEN
Nefera de Nile – NILE BLUE
Jackson Jekyll – YELLOW
Twyla – BLURPLE
Cleo de Nile – GOLD
Abbey Bominable – ICE BLUE
Clawd Wolf – TEAL
Draculaura – PINK
Skelita Calaveras – MARIGOLD

174

PAGES 92-93

WATZIT   CRESCENT   COUNT FABULOUS   HISSETTE   NEPTUNA   SIR HOOTS-A-LOT

PAGES 94-95

Name: Skelita Calaveras
Dead-scended from: Los Eskeletos
Scary-cool country: Mexico
My scare-itage: I am very proud of my scare-itage and its legends and traditions. My favourite custom is *Diá de los Muertos* (or Day of the Dead) where we honour our ancestors. We spend time with *la familia*, hold parties and decorate our homes with marigold flowers and screamily scrummy sugar skulls.

Name: Jinafire Long
Dead-scended from: Chinese Dragons
Scary-cool country: China
My scare-itage: The country of my fore-monsters is very eek-xotic, with customs and traditions that have been around for thousands and thousands of years. Monsters like me were often found guarding temples. We have always had great powers and can control elements including fire, wind and water.

Name: Cleo de Nile
Dead-scended from: The Mummy
Scary-cool country: Egypt
My scare-itage: My father tells me that, traditionally, monsters like me were entombed in pyramids in the middle of the desert with jewels and gold and sooo much bling. We still live in my father's pyramid and I have my own totes amazing crypt! Our bodies were wrapped in an OTT amount of bandages – the updated version of this look we now call 'bodycon'.

Name: Rochelle Goyle
Dead-scended from: The Gargoyles
Scary-cool city: Scaris
My scare-itage: Stone is a big part of my culture. My ancestors have always been found on and around great buildings, such as castles and cathedrals, which we protect. Although I come from Scaris, monsters like me are found in many countries, including Ancient Egypt and Greece. We can take many forms.

PAGE 96

1. Clawdeen Wolf, **2.** Jinafire Long,
3. Cleo de Nile, **4.** Spectra Vondergeist,
5. Ghoulia Yelps, **6.** Skelita Calaveras
7. Twyla

PAGE 97

1. EGYPTIAN PRINCESS – Cleo de Nile
2. WEREPUNK – Howleen Wolf
3. BOHO – Viperine Gorgon
4. TRIBAL PREP – Clawdia Wolf
5. BLIPSTER – Invisi Billy
6. FLOPPY CASUAL – HooDude Voodoo
7. JUNGLE CHIC – Jane Boolittle
8. PARTY CHICA – Skelita Calaveras
9. ROCK N ROLL GEEK – Wydowna Spider
10. GLAMOUR PUSS – Catty Noir

PAGES 98-99

1. False: she competes to be an apprentice for Madame Ghostier.
2. True, **3.** True, **4.** False: he keeps setting fire to things, including the students' work!, **5.** False, **6.** True,
7. False, **8.** True: Slo Mo wanted to buy something for Ghoulia., **9.** True,
10. Strange but true! , **11.** False: Cleo uses the youth potion, not Abbey.,
12. False: it's a necklace, not a bracelet., **13.** True, **14.** True, **15.** False,
16. False: her favourite colour is blurple, which is very different from purblue., **17.** True, **18.** False: she says it's really hard., **19.** True, **20.** True

PAGES 100-101

Name: Catrine de Mew
Loves: Scaris, bien sûr!
Killer style: Today my favourite colour it is lavender, but tomorrow, qui sait? There are so many colours inside the palette!

Name: Honey Swamp
Age: 115 in swamp monster years.
Killer style: My scaredrobe is filled with freakily feminine prints, skirts and dresses.

Name: Nefera de Nile
Age: Ageless, of course!
Loves: That's what little sisters are for!
Killer style: Anything gold totally rocks my tomb because it doesn't tarnish or rust, much like myself.

Name: Clawdia Wolf
Killer style: I like to mix graphic tribal prints with a preppy style to create a so of 'tribal prep' look. One year, Clawdee got me a manicure for my birthday, but on the way home I got an idea for a sto and had a bit of a chew ...

Name: *Elissabat a.k.a. Veronica Von Vamp*
Killer style: I'll wear anything frilly, as long as it's black or **purple**! I fangsolutely love my dangly **earrings** and knee-high boots, too.

Name: *Viperine Gorgon*
Killer style: I don't sssscale back when it comes to **mixing** different colours, patterns and fabricssss. Shopping for **make-up** is one of my favourite things to do and sometimes I even go to the elder monsters' **home** and do makeovers for the monsters there.

PAGE 102

PAGE 103

PAGES 104-105
1. FALSE – Skelita is from Hexico.
2. TRUE
3. TRUE
4. FALSE – she's a famous pop star.
5. TRUE – but she wants to help normies, not scare them!
6. FALSE – Meowlody is Purrsephone's twin.
7. FALSE – not after a millennium inside a lamp!
8. TRUE – she's a purr-fect artist.
9. TRUE
10. FALSE – her boy is Clawd Wolf!

PAGE 106

PAGE 108
owleen has a crush on Romulus.

PAGE 109

2	5	4	6	1	3
6	1	3	2	5	4
1	4	2	3	6	5
5	3	6	4	2	1
4	2	1	5	3	6
3	6	5	1	4	2

PAGE 110-111

PAGES 112-113
1. Frankie Stein, **2.** Draculaura,
3. Lagoona Blue, **4.** Ghoulia Yelps,
5. Spectra Vondergeist, **6.** Cleo de Nile,
7. Operetta, **8.** Abbey Bominable,
9. Clawdeen Wolf

Number of votes:
Spring = 1
Summer = 3
Autumn = 2
Winter = 2
No favourite = 1

The winning season is summer.

PAGE 116
1. Deuce Gorgon, **2.** Clawd Wolf,
3. Jackson Jekyll, **4.** Gil Webber,
5. Heath Burns, **6.** Slo Mo, **7.** Invisi Billy,
8. HooDude Voodoo, **9.** Holt Hyde,
10. Deuce Gorgon

PAGE 117
A. Clawdeen Wolf – Fashion stylist
B. Draculaura – Make-up artist
C. Abbey Bominable – Beautician
D. Ghoulia Yelps – Photographer
E. Cleo de Nile – Nail technician
F. Lagoona Blue – Model
G. Frankie Stein – Hairstylist

PAGES 118-119

Captain Penny, Shiver, Rhuen, Roux, Chewlian, Perseus

PAGES 120-121
1. Six, **2.** A coffin, **3.** Lagoona Blue,
4. Three, **5.** Draculaura,
6. Clawdeen Wolf, **7.** A lightning bolt,
8. Ghoulia's slippers, **9.** A mirror

PAGES 126-127
A. Frankie Stein, **B.** Deuce Gorgon,
C. Ghoulia Yelps, **D.** Draculaura, **E.** Abbey Bominable, **F.** Elissabat, **G.** Invisi Billy,
H. Slo Mo, **I.** Gil Webber, **J.** Heath Burns,
K. Headmistress Bloodgood,
L. Mr Hackington

PAGE 128

PAGE 129
1. IRIDESCENT SCREAM
2. FROSTY WHITE
3. CREEPY CRIMSON
4. SKULLTASTIC SCARLET
5. MARSHMALLOW MONSTER
6. TOFFEE APPLE
7. SHEER NIGHTMARE
8. ANTIQUE GREY
9. FANGTASTIC
10. DAMSEL IN DISTRESS
11. LOLLIPOP
12. STONE COLD
13. ELECTRIC BLUE

PAGES 130-131

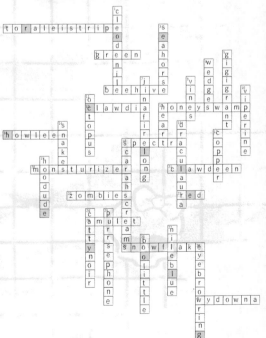

The ghoul who loves to mix rot iron and stained glass is Rochelle Goyle.

175

ANSWERS

PAGE 132

FAIL
TAIL
TALL
HALL
BALL
BAWL
BOWL
HOWL

PAGE 133

The Jungle Queen is Jane Boolittle.

PAGES 134–135

PAGE 138

PAGE 139

PAGE 142

PAGE 143

scowl; fowl; growl; howl; prowl

PAGES 146-147

a – Dustin
b – Memphis 'Daddy O' Longlegs'
c – Rhuen

PAGES 148-149

PAGE 152

1. TRUE, **2.** FALSE, **3.** FALSE, **4.** TRUE,
5. TRUE, **6.** FALSE, **7.** TRUE. **8.** FALSE,
9. TRUE, **10.** TRUE

PAGE 153

PAGE 154

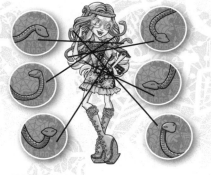

PAGE 155

1. Mechanical penguin, **2.** Venus flytrap,
3. Gargoyle griffin, **4.** Woolly mammoth,
5. Ghost ferret, **6.** Dust bunny, **7.** Gargoyle
bulldog, **8.** Scarab beetle

PAGES 158-159

Rochelle's words:
Rock Candy, Iron, Stained Glass,
Griffin, Protective, Architecture,
Grey, Sculpting, Roux, Scaris,
Pigeons, Disgruntled

Spectra's words:
Violet, Angel Cake, Curious, Persistent,
Floating, Transparent, Ghostly Gossip,
Journalism, Haunting, Chains, Pale, Kind,
Rhuen, Rattle, Silk, Defensive, Ferret

PAGE 161

35 bones

PAGE 162

PAGE 164

PAGE 166

Watch out for piranhas
in the pool!

PAGE 167

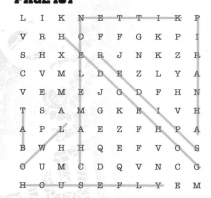

PAGE 168

A. Holt Hyde, **B.** Clawd Wolf, **C.** Deuce
Gorgon, **D.** HooDude Voodoo, **E.** Heath
Burns, **F.** Slo Mo

PAGE 172

1. B, **2.** D, **3.** C, **4.** E, **5.** A

TERROR-IFIC TALES

Unlife To Live

Ghoulia Yelps was studying on the school steps when....

Ghoulia, we're going for smoothies in free period. Want to join us?

Nurrgh!

O.M.Ra! You're not too busy, you're just sitting there like you do every day!

Suddenly a brain-shaped distress signal lit up the sky. Ghoulia sprang into action....

Ghoulia whisked the Headmistress to the salon and back....

Ghoulia! I need to get my hair done for the Superintendent's party tonight, but I'm swamped with paperwork....

Thanks Ghoulia, I look fabulous!

Next, there was an icy issue at the pool....

Is yours now.

Crikey, it's ffffreezing!

Doom At GLOOM BEACH

The ghouls were dissecting what they'd packed for their trip to Gloom Beach....

Is that enough?

Ten pairs of flats, nine boots, eight sandals....

But Cleo had more than fashion on her mind....

I hope you've saved room in there for your fearleading uniforms ... we have to win the Gloom Beach Spirit Staff!

It was a long journey and while the girls slept and dreamed....

How about a little song?

At last they arrived....

A ghoul could get used to this!

It's even m beautiful th I imagined

Unfortunately their cabin wasn't quite what they'd been expecting....

It's not that bad....

It's not exactly the Four Screamons.

It's a dump!

Cleo's fear squad were spending more time dusting than dancing....

None of the other girls are doing chores like us.

Those Smugsnorts Vampyr snobs will do anything to win!

Luckily Cleo and Ghoulia had worked out an ultra-hot routine....

That's right Ghoulia, it's been scientifically designed to win.

Uugh!

We start with a double jive handwheel....

Frankie began to film the routine on her iCoffin to show her parents. Unfortunately, the werecats were on the prowl....

I was just finishing my video letter to my folks.

Instead the creep showed the vid to the opposition....

Wanna watch t... Monster Hig... routine agai... Thought so...

I can mail it for you!

Later, Frankie had a visitor....

Frightday The 13th

Cleo and the ghouls were horrified to discover that Toralei was the new editor of the Fearbook …

... and mortalfied when she snapped them getting soaked by the werecat sisters.

Why didn't I know Toralei was running the Fearbook?

You're probably just out of the loop because fearleading took up so much time.

Out of the loop? I AM the loop!

Didn't you know, Cleo? Everyone's wearing boas.

Worried, Cleo tried using her father's cursed idols....

... but this just brought about a plague of frogs!

This can't be happening!

Mighty totem, fierce and mean, make me queen of the social scene.

I'll never regain my position atop the school social pyramid!

My ghouls and I are all over it! We're not afraid of anything.

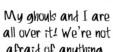

If anyone stayed overnight on Friday 13th, they'd be the talk of the school for sure!

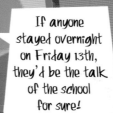

THE END

185

The Comic Clubbers, led by die-hard graphics-freak Ghoulia Yelps, have taken a lurk back at Monster High hiss-tory. Did you know that the school's unique student bodies didn't always skelebrate each other's differences?

Hiss-toria

Werewolf and vampire high schools have been at each other's throats for a thousand years....

Gggggggggggrrrrrr!

We transferred from an all-vampire school. It wasn't easy....

It can be said that the war ended here, at Monster High.

Vampires like Bram Devein and Gory Fangtell were new to Monster High.

Mwah Ha Ha Ha Ha!

Eeuurgh! You smell. Maybe it's time to use soap and water ... instead of your tongues.

Vampires made cutting comments to the werewolves....

We may have been a little rude.

This is our turf now, got it vam-poseurs?

We werewolves weren't any better....

Ha Ha Ha Haooooooowl!

The werewolves got aggressive ...

Garlic totally gives vampires mega monster zits!

... and mean to the vampires!

Aaaaargh! Garlic! Run for it!

It was so voltageously intense!

The smallest thing could set off a major battle....

This bathroom is now for vampires only.

You can't do that!

Did I see you growl at this vampire? Don't forget your place!

Grrrrrrrrr!

The atmosphere was horrifically tense!

The gym, sundown, bring your full strength!

Agreed. We can't go on like this!

Things hit breaking point.

But in time the vampires and werewolves realized that....

At Monster High what makes us unique brings us together, and together we can conquer the real enemy – prejudice!

Now vampire-werewolf relations have never been better!

Clawd, all I'm saying is you could have called me!

So now I howl too loud?!

You could have howled. Like when you're watching casketball and I'm trying to study!

You're cute when you're angry.

See!

THE END

187

Oh no!

Nefera!

BOOM!!!!!!

The Coffin Bean was trashed.

I don't suppose we broke Nefera's record?

We actually owe money for damages.

Talk about an epic fail!

Luckily optimistic Lagoona was on hand....

Nefera rushed in to laugh at the chaos.

You're not giving up are you?

To beat her we'd have to serve 500 customers in an hour.

Lagoona reminded them that together they did know at least 500.

Frankie felt defeated. She didn't even know 500 monsters!

The ghouls got on their iCoffins and started texting.

105 your order's ready! 106, 107, 108....

Nefera tried to stop the zombie rush to the Coffin Bean ...

The ghouls had done it!

Hurray! Our children's charity is going to be thrilled!

... but she got crushed in the stampede!

THE END

189

TOUGH AS SCALES

In the li-bury there are many ancient books, including the Monster High-clopedia, which details the many lessons the student bodies have learned as they pass through the school. Here are two such tales....

One day in metalwork class....

Killer job on the stand, Jinafire!

The fire-breathing daughter of the Chinese Dragon had welded a mount for the winning casketball.

This ball's irreplaceable!

Careful, Flame-brain!

But while the guys were arguing ...

... the ball bounced through a window and fell down a well!

Jinafire led the boys underground to find it.

Step aside. Let Manny show ya how it's done!

The boys were sure they could reach the ball.

We need to calculate the distance down and then ...

Ready, Wheeling and Able

Here's another tale from The Monster High-clopedia. It shows the important lesson a new student taught us about never judging a book by its cover!

One morning, the ghouls were discussing the new monster in school.

What's this new kid's name?

Rider — bet he's a natural athlete!

Clawd would break a leash to get another guy for Skultimate Roller Maze!

From the look of his blog, this kid's pretty intense!

Suddenly someone came flying round a corner....

Oh man! This place is spin-credible!

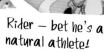

Oh hi! Monster High is totally a place where you can be yourself!

What're we gonna check out first?

Maybe we shouldn't show him ... all the sports stuff.

What if he got hurt?

Awesome, right?!

Penmanship class?

The worried ghouls took Rider somewhere safe....

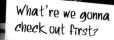

We've got some voltageous activities planned.

Li-bury Club, Wool Collecting Club, Rock and Pebble Society....

Frankie ran Rider through the most boring clubs at Monster High.

This is what you guys do for fun?

Rider was horrified!

I heard so much spooktacular stuff about Monster High, but none of it's true!

The ghouls looked everywhere for Rider.

I may have told him that Scream is the most epic thing you can possibly do!

Then Toralei slyly admitted she'd directed Rider towards the scream track.

Whooooo-hoooo!

Sure enough, Rider was burning rubber in the grim.

How could you let him on the scream track? It's not safe!

Draculaura rounded on Clawd.

Maybe he knows better than us what he can and can't do!

The werewolf told the ghouls that they were being over-protective.

Suddenly there was a crash!

The ghouls ran to check that Rider was okay....

That was totally spin-sane!!! I'm going again!

This is who I am. If I need help, I'll ask. Cool?

Rider reminded Frankie that she'd said he could be himself at Monster High.

Rider just wasn't a sit-around kinda dude!

Will you light my wheels on fire? I wanna try this again!

THE END

193

Student Disembodied President

Frankie Stein can't stand injustice at Monster High, but is she the beast candidate for Student Disembodied President?

One monstrous morning at Monster High ...

Can you zombies move any slower?!

... some zombies were causing tailbacks in the coffin corridor.

Poor zombies! They need their own lane in the hall.

The ghouls couldn't help feeling sorry for their slow-moving schoolmates.

Suddenly Frankie had a high-voltage brainwave.

I'm gonna run for Student Disembodied President, then I'll help them.

So the ghouls got to work promoting their GFF.

Cleo even agreed to be Frankie's campaign manager.

Frankie soon found their help came with strings attached....

You'll make my birthday a school holiday, right?

She thought things couldn't get more horrific ...

I just want you to lose.

... then she discovered Toralei was running against her.

Nevertheless, at Stein HQ, the ghouls were determined to help Frankie to victory.

STEIN HEADQUARTERS

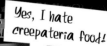

Draculaura was making slogan tees, while Ghoulia was getting ready to record the campaign commercial ...

... directed by Cleo of course!

TAKE 001 SCENE 001

DIRECTOR Cleo De Nile

Yes, I hate creepateria food!

Frankie explained her message....

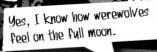

"Yes, I know how werewolves feel on the full moon."

"But what really leaves a bad taste in my mouth is our poor treatment of zombies."

The ghouls went off to drum up support for Frankie, so they didn't see Toralei sneakily fire-up Ghoulia's laptop.

Later that day....

Frankie! Look!

Toralei had sent her edited version of Frankie's film to everyone in school. It sounded as if Frankie hated werewolves and bad-mouthed zombies!

There was no time to do anything about Toralei's trick. The debate was on.

And voters, I'll also expand the car park!

You should hear from someone who has experienced injustice first hand.

Frankie explained she was running to give zombies a voice.

Poor thing!

The student bodies were moved to tears.

This breaks my heart.

Snnnifffff!

DEBATE

The audience burst into applause as Frankie urged them to stand with Slo Mo.

No one was surprised by the election result — except Toralei!

ELECTION RESULTS
67%
33%
0%

I told everyone to vote for Slo Mo. He's the best voice for the zombies.

You did the right thing!

Slo Mo was Student Disembodied President.

So ... about making my birthday a school holiday?

Lucky him!

THE END

195

Scarah-voyant

When Scarah Screams sets her sights on dating Invisi Billy it takes some monster matchmaking from her fiends to make it happen....

The ghouls were fanging out in the coffin corridor ...

... when Scarah Screams came walking by.

Hey Scarah, what number am I thinking of?

Frankie loved testing Scarah's psychic skills ...

Scarah admitted it was Invisi Billy she liked.

I don't know ... one - the loneliest number?

All right Scarah, which boy has you all wrapped up?

... but today Scarah seemed somewhat out of sorts.

Buzz Wingman?

Golden ghoul Cleo knew exactly what the problem was.

Draculaura told him everything.

Draculaura suggested Scarah go and talk to him ...

If I get too close I'd hear what he's thinking. What if I heard he doesn't like me?

'ssup?

Just then Clawd turned up.

Well, Invisi Billy and Scarah would make a perfect couple except she's too shy and Billy's too quiet and ...

Clawd promised to talk to Billy.

But she didn't dare.

But Billy had the same doubts as Scarah.

Luckily Frankie came up with a brilliant idea ...

Clawd caught up with Billy in the creepateria.

I heard about you and Scarah.

I'm afraid that if I get too close she'll read my mind and see I like her and that might freak her out.

Oooh! I think I know how to fix this.

What did you hear?

That you like her.

I can't!

You gotta be transparent with her.

... which used Scarah's mind-reading abilities.

First Clawd cornered Billy in the grimnasium.

Bad news bro. Scarah's already got a date in the graveyard tonight.

Then Cleo found Draculaura in the ghouls' toilets.

Billy has a date tonight in the graveyard.

Scarah will be devastated.

She reminded the vampire not to tell Scarah anything.

But Draculaura bumped straight into Scarah.

Is something wrong?

No, I don't know anything.

Poor Draculaura couldn't help thinking about Invisi Billy's date and Scarah read her mind.

Billy has a date? With who?

I'm late for class!

That night the graveyard was deserted …

… except for a picnic blanket and hamper.

Two figures tiptoed towards each other and …

Oh!

… collided.

Billy and Scarah were confused.

I guess your date will be here soon.

My date? You mean your date?

Then they realized their fiends had set them up!

I like you.

I like you, too!

Next morning in school....

Scarah smiled at her monster matchmaking friends.

Draculaura couldn't believe her eyes.

Wha...? They're together? Okay, I'm confused.

I didn't say a word.

It's not easy to surprise a telepath!

We just told Draculaura it was a secret!

Can I walk you to class?

You read my mind!

And they lived telepathically ever after!

197

The Stitchuation

Spectra was on the steps of Monster High writing her blog.

Time for the Ghostly Gossip to tell the ghouls what's hot and what's not....

Hold your horses, look at the Mustang that just pulled up!

Suddenly a handsome centaur trotted past.

There's a handsome new guy trotting the howlways of Monster High! He's got Operetta and Toralei in a spooky spin....

Frankie was excited by the news.

A new boy!

Oh no! More competition!

Jackson Jekyll was not!

Huh? Wow!

Within seconds Spectra had updated her blog.

Frankie's bolts fizzed with volts as the handsome half-horse passed by.

But she wasn't the only ghoul with her eye on the new boy.

Operetta couldn't wait to make her move.

Well hey, sugar. Fancy meeting a colt like you in a school like this.

But the gorgeous centaur just kept walking.

Toralei was full of scorn.

Oh what a clumsy kitty.

Aaargh!

Nice try, country mouse. Let me show you how it's done.

She approached Archer and pretended to drop her books ...

... but instead of helping her, Archer knocked her flying with his tail.

198

He is so mine!

I'll have him chomping at the bit by lunch.

Dream on.

The ghouls faced off!

Next, Toralei played the sympathy card.

I wish someone would help poor little me down these stairs.....

To no avail.

I'm gonna trot on over there and have me a lunch date!

Toralei was spitting mad! She bared her claws at her love rival.

Keep your claws off him, he's mine!

Splat! Operetta threw a pie at the werecat.

You did not!

Within seconds the red-haired rockabilly found herself on the wrong end of a batburger.

There was nothing for it, but a full-on creepateria food fight.

We have to stop this!

Are you nuts?

And ruin our lunchtime entertainment?

Covered in food, the ghouls decided to settle the problem once and for all.

Okay, which one of us do you like?

Archer's eyes lit up.

But it seemed his affections lay elsewhere ...

... with Nightmare!

You can have him, he ain't my type.

No thanks, I've got more horse sense than that!

THE END

199

CLAWBACKS

When both Cleo and Toralei vie for the lead in the school production of *The Wizard Of Ooze* all howl breaks loose.

It was school production time at Monster High ...

Hey Cleo!

Toralei, I barely saw you there. I mean you're just sooo forgettable!

... and claws were out on the coffin corridor.

You've got no chance at getting the lead role.

I was born to play Gore-athy in *The Wizard Of Ooze!*

The fight for the lead role was on!

You're older than the pyramids ... this is a part for a young monster, like me! Good luck — grandmummy!

Toralei had the last catty meow.

Grandmummy? Wait ... that's it!

This gave Cleo an idea.

My grandmummy!

In her locker was a bottle of potion her grandmummy had given her.

Looking at the bottle she heard her grandmummy's words....

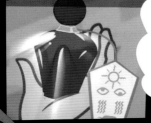

In this bottle is magical water from the fountain of youth!

Gore-athy is as good as mine!

She dabbed the potion on her neck.

On stage the newly youthful Cleo gave the audition of her life.

Mr Where was stunned.

Outstanding Cleo, so vibrant, such enthusiasm!

Toralei, however, wasn't so easily impressed.

There's something seriously fishy going on with that ghoul!

Toralei watched from the rafters as Cleo doused herself in youth potion.

Toralei!

I knew it!

The furious kitty leapt down and confronted her rival.

Paws off!

Give me some!

A cat-fight ensued.

What's going on?

They are acting like hungry yaks at meal time.

Frankie and Abbey looked on in surprise ...

I need to be younger!
No, I need to be younger!

... as the silly ghouls fought over the bottle ...

... which flew into the air and soaked them both in potion!

The magical glow eventually faded to reveal two tiny beings.

Oh no! We're monster babies.

The monster babies were not happy!

There was nothing the ghouls could do but go on stage for their clawbacks as babies.

Luckily Mr Where had good news for the ghouls.

... with two teeny tiny co-stars.

On performance night, the curtains opened to reveal Venus McFlytrap as Gore-athy ...

Fierce Crush

Howleen Wolf finds out that love can be fur-rociously tricky when she falls for an older werewolf....

It was the first full moon of the Lunar Leap Year ...

Wear my ring?

... and romance was in the air.

My Clawsity Jacket?

Oh Clawd!

Wear my flea collar?

Everyone was feeling loved....

Everyone, that is, except Howleen.

Don't go fallin' into that 'I gotta get a boyfriend' trap!

Clawdeen told Howleen she was way too young for boys.

I'm not, I'm not, I'm not, I'M NOT!!!!!

Hi Rom!

Just then Romulus came over…

... and gallantly opened Howleen's rusty locker.

Wow!

You are barking up the wrong tree sis – he used to puppy-sit you!

… the students gathered for Full Moon Sports Day.

Welcome to Monster High's Full Moon Sports Day!

Yay Team!

Howleen took the opportunity to open up to her friend.

I really like him Lothar.

Did Romulus like her, too?

Lothar knew just what unrequited love was like!

He had it bad for Howleen.

But Howleen just didn't notice.

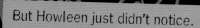

How can I make him notice me?

Do the things he likes to do.

She was too wrapped up in Romulus!

Howleen knew Romulus liked sticks …

Hey, those are for the bonfire!

… so she borrowed one.

She threw it for Romulus.

Sadly, it was shaped like a boomerang.

It soared straight back towards the fire …

No!

Not this way!

Howleen had no choice but to douse him with water.

Are you okay?

… and Romulus followed.

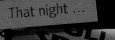
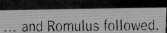

FIELD OF SCREAMS

Toralei and the Werecat twins have a purr-fect plan for stopping the ghouls beating them in the corn maze race … or do they?

Dawn broke in the grounds of Monster High.

Frankie and her fiends headed for the corn maze.

Who's ready for some voltageous fun?

Frankie had the map.

Everyone seemed unsure.

A race through a maze?

I do not 'race' anywhere!

Then Gil Webber piped up.

The winning team gets their picture in *The Gory Gazette!*

Who's in the lead now?

The scheming kitty rocked up to gloat!

They looked at the scoreboard … Toralei!

You flea-brains really think you're going to beat our time?

Your record is history!

They entered the vast, spooky maze …

… but it wasn't long before they were lost.

Left does look shorter!

What do you think, Lagoona?

Heath got hungry.

Popcorn, anyone?

He decided to pop some corn himself …

… accidentally setting fire to the map.

HEATH!!!!

Whatever....

No map, no record!

How would they win now?

I hope we can find our way out!

Perched in a tree, Toralei grinned devilishly.

We've been wandering around here forever!

It's been four minutes, love.

Suddenly, Manny Taur thundered past.

Finally, some luck!

He's a minotaur! They're bonza at mazes – he can lead us out!

They followed Manny.

Manny was running so fast...

... he didn't notice Toralei with arms of corn.

Toralei threw corn on the path ...

What...?

Hey!

... which attracted flocks of crows.

Luckily they could still see Manny's hoofprints.

The gang followed the trail.

Into the path of Toralei ...

Go, get 'em boys!

... who released some wild beasts.

Now the ghouls had devil hounds on their tail.

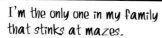

Suddenly they came upon Manny, crying.

I'm the only one in my family that stinks at mazes.

The minotaur admitted he too, was lost ...

... and that he was frightened by 'scary things' in the maze.

Run!!!!

NO Ghouls ALLOWED

When Clawd Wolf suddenly cancels his date with Draculaura she smells a rat! Just what does 'Guys' Night Out' involve?

Draculaura was freaked out.

> I can't make it tonight. I'm ... er ... studying with Romulus.

Clawd had cancelled their date.

The cute vampire told her ghoulfriends what had happened.

Clawd and Deuce promised to help Mr Hack repaint his hearse.

> No! They're all going to Gil's to work on that rap album.

They soon realized the boys were up to something.

But what exactly?

> Look, tonight is our guys' night out....

> No ghouls allowed.

They decided to find out just what the guys had planned so they ...

... intercepted notes ...

The guys had been angrily talking about 'battle strategy', leading the ghouls to a horrible conclusion....

... eavesdropped ...

... and even did some underwater surveillance.

> They're going to fight!

They tracked the guys to a graveyard and peeped over the stones.

> Level 4 lasers, right through your defences!

> Boys are so weird ... but they're adorable!

> This is hilarious!

Were the guys really fighting?

In fact, 'Guys' Night' involved a very nerdy game!

The ghouls decided to make a night of it!

THE END

Tortoise & the Scare

Shuffling zombie Ghoulia Yelps may not be the freaky-fastest ghoul in school, but she sure is scary smart. So what happened when Monster High's mean ghoul Toralei Stripe challenged Ghoulia to a race?

One day in the coffin corridor, Ghoulia tapped Toralei on the shoulder.

Whatever it is, make it fast ... oh wait, you can't, you're a zombie.

Hey! She was just trying to invite you to her party!

She was trying to be nice!

Clawdeen, Frankie and the ghouls overheard and stuck up for their friend.

But Toralei carried on making fun of zombies.

Let me guess, it starts at eight, but the zombies don't get there 'til eleven!

To prove her point, Toralei challenged Ghoulia to a race across school.

If you win, I'll serve food at your party. If I win, you serve at one of mine!

The ghouls tried to think of ways to help their friend ...

We could get Toralei to chase this laser pointer down the wrong hall....

This is cheating!

I can hit her with pies! Be pretty funny....

... but Frankie thought Ghoulia should rise to the challenge alone.

Toralei was so confident she'd win she even stopped to boast.

I've got a purr-fect headline for your Ghostly Gossip blog - 'Zombies Serve Kitties At High-End Soirée!'

Meanwhile in the catacombs, Ghoulia was busy tickling the dragon's nostrils until ...

Aaatchoooo

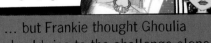

... the beast sneezed her right across school!

By the time Toralei sauntered into class....

Wha...? What? How?

Clever Ghoulia was hard at work.

Later, while Ghoulia threw some shapes on the dance floor at her party ...

... waitress Toralei had to eat her words ...

... and a little pie, too!

THE END

Tree of Unlife

Venus had her tendrils in a twist.

Cleo! Huge emergency!

Careful! They're designer!

She needed some bandages from Cleo's spare stash.

The ghouls found Venus with a very sick tree.

... followed by Frankie and Abbey.

She told us to bring the largest thermometer we could find.

As Venus sped off, Lagoona showed up ...

You seen Venus? She told me to bring her 3,000 cc of distilled water...

What was Venus up to?

Hang in there, big guy!

First she used Abbey's thermometer to take the tree's temperature.

Cleo was horrified!

Quick! We don't have much time!

Then she used Lagoona's water on the tree's roots.

Ohhh! My Ghostier bandages!!!

Venus explained the severity of the situation.

Cleo! This is the oldest living tree at Monster High. He's been here for hundreds of years.

Venus sobbed that the precious tree was dying.

What wrong with it — er ... I mean him?

I've tried everything....

Someone must know what to do ... a teacher, a scientist?

Mother Nature! She'll know.

Venus led the ghouls to a secret lake.

She asked Mother Nature's advice about the Great Oak.

Remember what the tree has been to you....

Mother Nature told them to love the tree back to life.

Call Cleo and tell her to get every monster in school out by the tree, ASAP!

Cleo did as Venus asked.

Everyone gathered around the sick tree.

Why are we standing by this overgrown piece of firewood?

The tree may have been sick, but he still didn't like being insulted.

Venus explained the tree was a living history of themselves.

Frankie reminded Ghoulia she used to study by the tree.

I wrote some of my best stories under this tree.

Uggrr huhh!

I lost five soccer balls in its branches.

The zombie gave the Oak a nostalgic squeeze.

And Clawd and I came here on our first date — see?

Soon everyone was sharing memories.

The student bodies had loved the tree back to full health.

With every lovely memory, more leaves sprouted on the tree's branches.

Look!

Until....

It was time for a creeperific celebration!

THE END

ANGRY GHOULS

Clawsome new app *Angry Ghouls* has Monster High in a trance. Can old-fashioned ghoul, Robecca Steam, break the spell?

One grim day at Monster High ...

Why don't you get an iCoffin?

I like my old typewriter. It gets the job done.

... Robecca Steam and Draculaura were debating the merits of old inventions versus new technology.

Draculaura explained that free games could be downloaded onto an iCoffin.

Within seconds she was hooked on *Angry Ghouls*.

I wonder why Draculaura didn't show up to class.

I hope she's okay.

She was so engrossed she forgot all about her lessons.

Frankie, Clawdeen and Robecca confronted their vampire fiend.

Did you miss class because of this game?

Clawdeen took Draculaura's phone but instantly became hooked on the game herself!

There's some kinda witch ghoul coming at me.

Just hurl a potion bottle at her.

Robecca tried to speak to Clawd about the problem, but he too was in a trance.

You ghouls have been playing for like, EVER!

More and more monsters were being sucked in.

Even sensible Frankie succumbed to the lure of *Angry Ghouls*.

oooOh!

Mr Rotter was not amused to find Frankie playing games in class.

You can pick up your little gadget from Miss Bloodgood's office later.

Oh! What an interesting looking game.

Soon everyone's grades began to slip.

Look, new high score!

Robecca was steaming mad!

It seemed she was the only monster unimpressed by the game.

When Mr Hack was so distracted he let an experiment explode, Robecca knew she had to act.

She needed a high-tech ghoul to help.

Ghoulia! I need your help.

Ghoulia was so addicted to the game, she paid no attention!

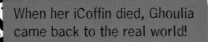

When her iCoffin died, Ghoulia came back to the real world!

So, Robecca shook Ghoulia hard and her iCoffin battery fell out.

Robecca explained that they needed to put a stop to the *Angry Ghouls* epidemic.

You're transmitting a virus to all other devices? Splendid!

Ghoulia's scheme worked. *Angry Ghouls* was wiped from every iCoffin.

Oh! Game over, I guess!

Until....

Yo! I got this rockin' new app. It's even better than *Angry Ghouls!*

The student bodies came out of their gaming coma.

... with two obviously irritated exceptions.

Within seconds, every student body was staring at a screen again ...

Oh drear!

THE END

Inscare-itance

Grandmummy de Nile is keen to pass on her most valuable treasure to the granddaughter who proves her undying love. Will Cleo or Nefera triumph?

It was just another night in the crypt for the de Nile sisters.

You so owe me!

Consider it payback!

The dynastic duo were embroiled in their latest row ...

Riiing, Riiing

... when they were interrupted by a slave bringing the phone.

I got it!

No, it's for me!

As usual, they fought over who should answer it.

In fact, the call was for both ghouls.

Hello ghouls, it's your grandmummy.

Surely their grandmummy wouldn't be coming to visit?

Sadly she was, but she wasn't coming empty-handed.

I will give my most valuable treasure to the granddaughter who shows me she loves me the most.

Cleo immediately began her campaign to win the treasure ...

... by having an army of servants prepare a feast.

Nefera jealously watched Cleo's cooks parade a stream of delicious dishes. She'd only prepared one cupcake.

So she unleashed a plague of locusts ...

... which swiftly devoured Cleo's feast.

Undeterred, Cleo had the servants prepare a beautiful garden for Grandmummy.

Nefera had other plans.

In no time, Nefera's servants had dug a river through the middle of Cleo's garden.

Next Cleo had her servant paint an enormous mural of Grandmummy.

She even signed it …

The Pharaohs' curse upon you Nefera.

… just before Nefera defaced it with a moustache and beard.

Mwah, ha ha!

Poor Cleo had one last chance to prove herself worthy of Grandmummy's gift.

I know that Grandmummy collects these ancient jars.

You know what else she loves? Bowling!

I hereby give my most valuable treasure to Nefera!

Cleo was knocked flying and her jars smashed.

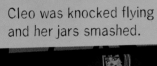

Just then, Grandmummy de Nile arrived by boat via Nefera's special river.

Yesss!

She immediately named her 'chosen one'.

Gloating Nefera threw open the treasure chest to find …

… the snarling, snapping Dog of the Dead!

Later that afternoon the perfect peace of the pyramid was only broken by …

… Nefera and her 'little treasure'.

THE END

CREATURE OF THE YEAR

There's an unexpected ogre-achiever at Monster High, but which faculty member will be chosen for Creature of the Year?

Headmistress Bloodgood called the ghouls to her office.

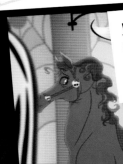

Ladies, it's time for Monster High to pick its annual Creature of the Year!

I've narrowed it down to two members of the Faculty.

The headmistress asked the ghouls to help her choose the winner.

... either Mr Hack ...

... or Mr Rotter.

There was a gasp of horror from the ghouls.

Lagoona was the first to speak.

Well it can't be Mr Hack – he's anti-phibean!

The bathing beauty showed the headmistress a memory.

They'd once been asked to nurture gargoyle eggs.

Maybe you should swap partners – everyone knows sea monsters are bad parents.

Mr Hack had insulted Lagoona.

Cleo agreed Mr Hack didn't deserve an award.

He takes royal delight in our misery.

She reminded them of the time he'd driven them …

Your cabin is in a slightly different location.

… to Gloom Beach for fearleading trials.

He'd laughed himself half to death …

It's, er, not that bad?

… at the fact they were staying in a dump.

All things considered …

YOU FAILED!

YOU FAILED!

Mwah Hah Haaaa!

… everyone agreed that the mad science teacher …

Off with their grades!

… was not quite the ticket!

That settles it, Mr Rotter it is!

The headmistress announced her decision.

Cleo was equally outraged at this suggestion.

Mr Rotter I did the work to perfection — why didn't I get an A?

I DON'T GIVE As!!

Frankie reminded everyone about Mr Rotter's other failings.

Remember when he gave us all detention?